Selected p–Block Elements

First published 1984
by John Murray (Publishers) Ltd
50 Albemarle Street
London W1X 4BD

Printed and bound in Great Britain by
Martin's of Berwick

British Library Cataloguing in Publication Data

Independent Learning Project for Advanced
Chemistry
Selected *p*-Block Elements. - (ILPAC; Unit I6)
1. Science
I. Title   II. Series
500   Q161.2

ISBN 0 7195 4054 2

CONTENTS

PREFACE

This volume is one of twenty Units produced by ILPAC, the Independent Learning Project for Advanced Chemistry, written for students preparing for the Advanced Level examinations of the G.C.E. The Project has been sponsored by the Inner London Education Authority and the materials have been extensively tested in London schools and colleges. In its present revised form, however, it is intended for a wider audience; the syllabuses of all the major Examination Boards have been taken into account and questions set by these boards have been included.

Although ILPAC was initially conceived as a way of overcoming some of the difficulties presented by uneconomically small sixth forms, it has frequently been adopted because its approach to learning has certain advantages over more traditional teaching methods. Students assume a greater responsibility for their own learning and can work, to some extent, at their own pace, while teachers can devote more time to guiding individual students and to managing resources.

By providing personal guidance, and detailed solutions to the many exercises, supported by the optional use of video-cassettes, the Project allows students to study A-level chemistry with less teacher-contact time than a conventional course demands. The extent to which this is possible must be determined locally; potentially hazardous practical work must, of course, be supervised. Nevertheless, flexibility in time-tabling makes ILPAC an attractive proposition in situations where classes are small or suitably-qualified teachers are scarce.

In addition, ILPAC can provide at least a partial solution to other problems. Students with only limited access to laboratories, for example, those studying at evening classes, can concentrate upon ILPAC practical work in the laboratory, in the confidence that related theory can be systematically studied elsewhere. Teachers of A-level chemistry who are inexperienced, or whose main discipline is another science, will find ILPAC very supportive. The materials can be used effectively where upper and lower sixth form classes are timetabled together. ILPAC can provide 'remedial' material for students in higher education. Schools operating sixth form consortia can benefit from the cohesion that ILPAC can provide in a fragmented situation. The project can be adapted for use in parts of the world where there is a severe shortage of qualified chemistry teachers. And so on.

A more detailed introduction to ILPAC, with specific advice both to students and to teachers, is included in the first volume only. Details of the Project Team and Trial Schools appear inside the back cover.

LONDON 1983

ACKNOWLEDGEMENTS

Thanks are due to the following examination boards for permission to reproduce questions from past A-level papers:

Joint Matriculation Board

Teacher-marked Exercises, p12(1977), p38(1979), p49(1978)

Oxford & Cambridge Schools Examination Board

Teacher-marked Exercise, p46(1979)

Oxford Delegacy of Local Examinations

Exercise 28(1981)
Level One Test 2a(1980), 2d(1977), 8(1981), 10b(1981)

Southern Universities Joint Board

Exercises 21(1976), 38(1975), 53(1975)
Level One Test 1(1980), 5(1981), 7(1976), 11(1981), 12(1981 & 1975)
End-of-Unit Test (1975)

The Associated Examining Board

Exercises 25(1979), 52(1980), 69(1980)
Teacher-marked Exercise p70(1981)
Level One Test 6(1981)

University of Cambridge Local Examinations Syndicate

Exercise 32(1974)
Level One Test 2c(1981), 4a(1980), 4b(1974), 10a(1979)

University of London School Examinations Department

Exercises 4a(1979), 4b & 4c(1978), 10(N1980), 22(N1976), 36(N1977), 65(N1978), 70(N1974), 71(N1976), 72(1980), 75(1980)
Level One Test 2b(1978), 3(1980), 9(1980)
End-of-Unit Test 2(1982), 3(1976), 4(1976)
End-of-Unit Practical Test (1977)

Where answers to these questions are included, they are provided by ILPAC and not by the examination boards.

The article on pages 62 to 64 is reproduced from 'Education in Chemistry', May 1982, by permission of the Royal Society of Chemistry.

Photographs are included by permission as follows:

Fig. 3, page 9 - Tony Langham, by courtesy of the British Aluminium Company Ltd.
Fig. 5, page 14 - British Railways Board, Central Photographic Unit.
Fig. 11, page 27 - Southend General Hospital.
Fig. 12, page 35 - J. Allan Cash Photolibrary.
Fig. 15, page 41 - Geoff Cox.
Fig. 19, page 67 - British Aluminium Company Ltd.
Fig. 24, page 74 - ICI Agricultural Division.
Photographs of students and Fig. 6 - Tony Langham.

SYMBOLS USED IN ILPAC UNITS

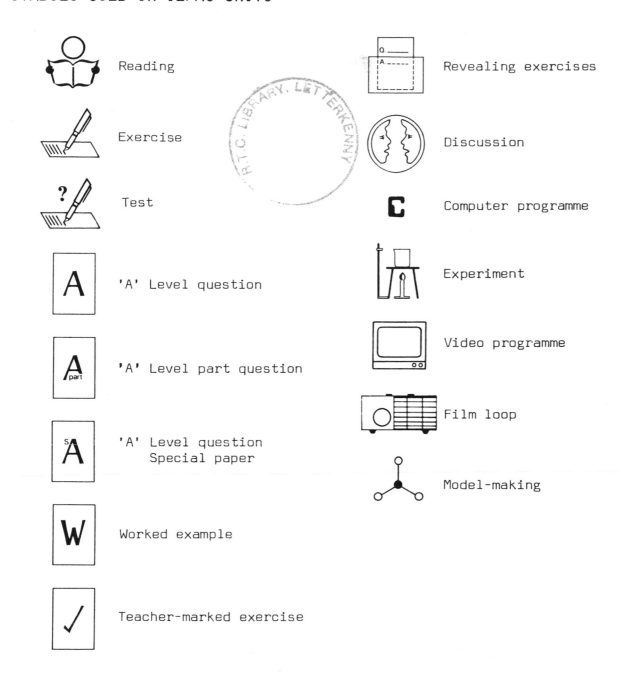

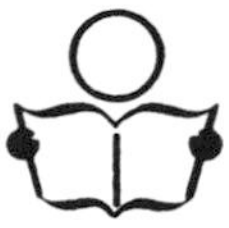

Reading

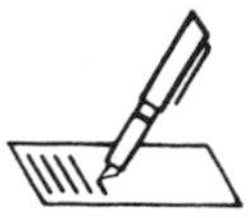

Exercise

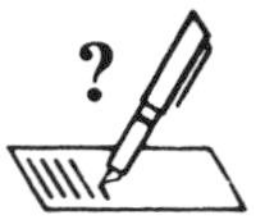

Test

'A' Level question

'A' Level part question

'A' Level question
Special paper

Worked example

Teacher-marked exercise

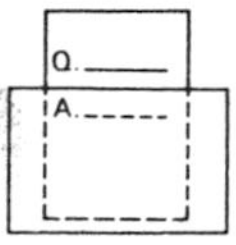

Revealing exercises

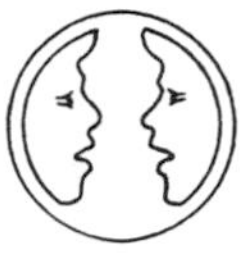

Discussion

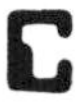

Computer programme

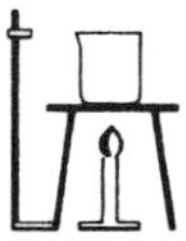

Experiment

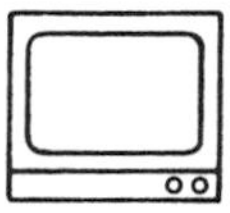

Video programme

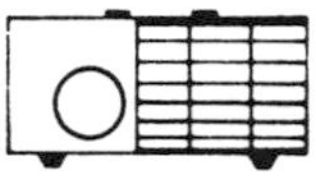

Film loop

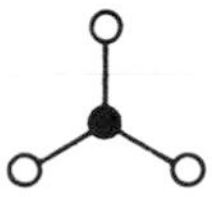

Model-making

INTERNATIONAL HAZARD SYMBOLS

 Harmful

 Flammable

 Corrosive

 Toxic

 Explosive

 Oxidising

 Radioactive

INTRODUCTION

In this Unit we deal with Groups III, V and VI, as shown in the outline Periodic Table below.

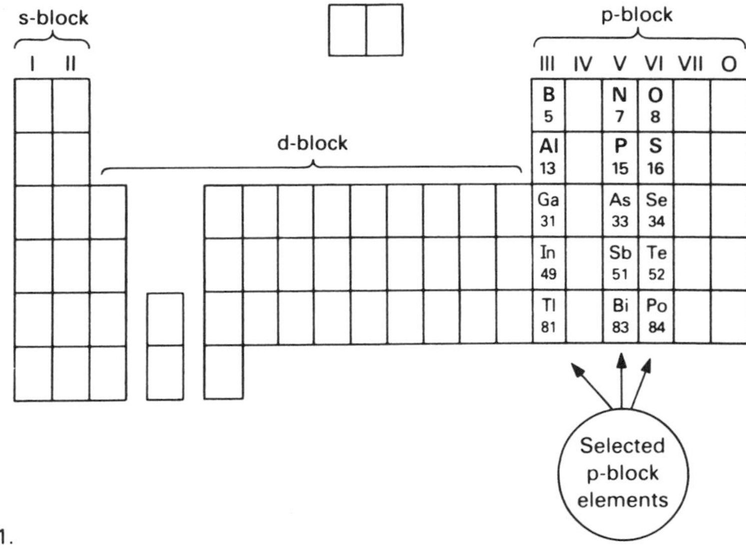

Fig. 1.

The elements in these groups show the usual gradation from non-metallic to metallic properties with increasing atomic number.

The chemistry of the first two elements in each group will be treated in detail in Level One. We include a brief account of the chemistry of the remaining elements in each group only in so far as it illustrates group trends.

In Level Two we deal with the industrial manufacture of some elements and compounds from these groups.

The Unit as a whole covers a great deal of chemistry; it is unlikely that you will need to study all of it. Consult your teacher if you are not clear about what is required for your syllabus.

There are five experiments in this Unit, three of them in Level One, one in Level Two and one as an end-of-Unit practical test.

PRE-KNOWLEDGE

Before you start work on this Unit you should be able to:

(1) explain the terms

(a) amphoteric,

(b) lattice energy,

(c) electronegativity,

(d) oxidation number,

(e) hydrogen bonding,

(f) polarization of both bonds and ions;

(2) describe the action of heat and of an alkali on ammonium chloride;

(3) describe a test for sulphate ions in solution;

(4) outline the preparation of hydrogen peroxide;

(5) deduce the shapes of molecules by means of the electron-pair repulsion theory;

(6) explain why solutions of iron(III) salts are acidic;

(7) use standard electrode potentials to predict the outcome of chemical reactions and to write conventional cell diagrams;

(8) use Le Chatelier's principle to predict the effect on an equilibrium system of changing the conditions;

(9) perform calculations using the expression for the equilibrium constant, K_p, for a chemical reaction.

PRE-TEST

1. Explain, by reference to the mutual repulsion of electron pairs, the shapes of the molecules of ammonia, NH_3, and boron trifluoride, BF_3. How do these substances react together? (6)

2. Zinc oxide, ZnO, is amphoteric. Explain this statement, illustrating your answer with two ionic equations. (3)

3. When a white solid, X, is heated with dilute sodium hydroxide solution, a gas, Y, is evolved which turns damp red litmus blue. An aqueous solution of X gives a white precipitate with silver nitrate solution.

   (a) Identify X and Y and give equations for the two reactions mentioned. (4)

   (b) Describe, with an equation, what happens when X is heated alone. (3)

4. Outline the preparation of aqueous hydrogen peroxide, starting from barium metal. (3)

5. The lattice energy of magnesium chloride is -2489 kJ mol^{-1}. Write the relevant thermochemical equation. (2)

6. What two structural features must a substance possess in order to form hydrogen bonds between its molecules? (3)

7. Hydrogen fluoride is usually regarded as covalent, but it shows a significant degree of ionic character. Explain this statement briefly, using the terms 'electronegative' and 'polarization' in your answer. (3)

8. Calculate the oxidation number of nitrogen in each of the following:

   (a) NH_3, (b) HNO_3, (c) NO_2^-. (3)

9. What is the formula of the most numerous of the complex ions in a solution of iron(III) nitrate in water? Explain briefly why this solution is acidic. (4)

10. Describe a simple test for sulphate ions in solution. Write an equation. (3)

Continued overleaf.

11. Standard electrode potentials for two half-cells are as follows:

$Cd^{2+}(aq) + 2e^- \rightleftharpoons Cd(s)$; $E^\ominus = -0.40$ V

$Ag^{+}(aq) + e^- \rightleftharpoons Ag(s)$; $E^\ominus = +0.80$ V

(a) Which is more readily oxidized, cadmium or silver? (1)

(b) Deduce an equation for the reaction which occurs between one of the metals and the aqueous ions of the other metal. (1)

(c) Write a conventional cell diagram for a cell in which the reaction in (b) occurs. What is its e.m.f? (State the sign.) (2)

12. The formation of ammonia is represented by the thermochemical equation:

$N_2(g) + 3H_2(g) \rightleftharpoons 2NH_3(g)$; $\Delta H^\ominus = -94.6$ kJ mol^{-1}

(a) Use Le Chatelier's principle to deduce the effect on this equilibrium of increasing (i) pressure, and (ii) temperature. (4)

(b) Write an expression for the equilibrium constant, K_p. (1)

(c) A mixture of hydrogen and nitrogen in the molar ratio 3:1 was allowed to reach equilibrium at 100 atm and 400 °C. The equilibrium mixture contained 25% ammonia. Calculate the value of K_p under these conditions. (4)

(Total 50 marks)

LEVEL ONE

GROUP III: BORON AND ALUMINIUM

In Units I1 (The *s*-Block Elements) and I2 (The Halogens), you learned that the top element in each group is atypical. Similarly, in Group III, you might expect boron to differ significantly from aluminium.

In the first section we consider the properties of the elements in Group III, with particular reference to comparisons between boron and aluminium.

The nature of the elements

Boron and aluminium are too reactive to be found free in nature. Boron occurs principally in borates, the most important being sodium tetraborate (borax), $Na_2B_4O_7 \cdot 10H_2O$, and as borosilicates. Aluminium occurs in a variety of aluminosilicates and its hydrated oxide. It is the most abundant metal in the earth's crust, as shown in Fig. 2.

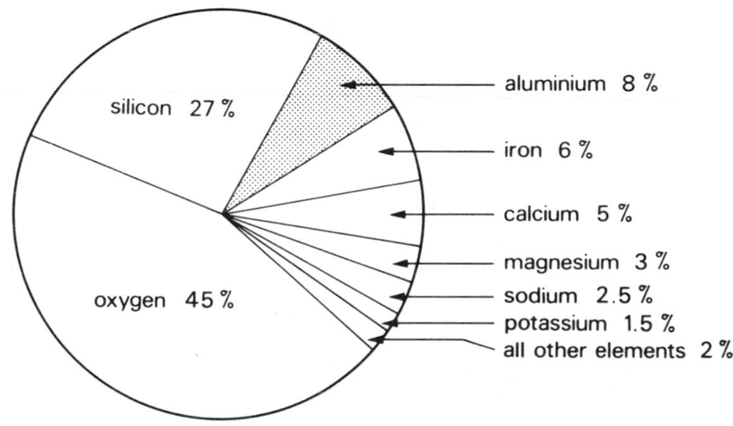

Fig. 2. Composition of the earth's crust

Objectives. When you have finished this section, you should be able to:

(1) compare physical properties of boron and aluminium, such as appearance, conductivity and ionic radii;

(2) list the likely oxidation states of the elements in Group III;

(3) state how aluminium reacts with acids and alkalis;

(4) explain how aluminium sulphate can be prepared from aluminium.

To obtain a simple overall picture of Group III, we suggest that you read the introduction to these elements in your textbook(s). Pay particular attention to their appearance, their electrical conductivity and the ores from which boron and aluminium are extracted. This will help you to do the following exercises.

Exercise 1 (a) Name the ore from which aluminium is extracted. What compound is the main constituent of this ore?

(b) Describe the appearance and electrical conductivity of boron and aluminium.

(c) What does your answer to (b) suggest about the metallic character of these two elements?

(d) What would you expect to be the appearance and electrical conductivity of thallium?

(Answers on page **86**)

We discuss the extraction of aluminium from its ore in detail in Level Two. The next exercise is related to the atomic properties of Group III elements.

Exercise 2 (a) Write the electronic configurations of boron and aluminium using the s, p, d notation.

(b) What oxidation states would you expect boron and aluminium to exhibit?

(c) Would you expect to encounter the 'inert pair effect' in this group? Explain your answer.

List the possible oxidation states of thallium.

(d) (i) Record the ionic radii of boron and aluminium from your data book. How do they compare with other ionic radii?

(ii) Would you expect to find many compounds containing B^{3+} or Al^{3+} ions? Explain, with reference to your answer to (i).

(Answers on page **86**)

In the next exercise you make some predictions about the reactions of aluminium by referring to standard electrode potentials. These reactions are important in relation to the extensive use of aluminium in manufacturing.

Exercise 3 By reference to the standard electrode potentials, $E^{\ominus}$, listed below, predict whether aluminium will react with:

(a) dilute hydrochloric acid,

(b) dilute sodium hydroxide solution.

Electrode reaction	$E^{\ominus}$/V
1. $Al^{3+}(aq) + 3e^- \rightleftharpoons Al(s)$	-1.66
2. $Al(OH)_4^-(aq) + 3e^- \rightleftharpoons Al(s) + 4OH^-(aq)$	-2.35
3. $2H^+(aq) + 2e^- \rightleftharpoons H_2(g)$	0.00
4. $2H_2O(l) + 2e^- \rightleftharpoons H_2(g) + 2OH^-(aq)$	-0.83

(Answers on page **86**)

You can test your predictions in the next experiment.

EXPERIMENT 1

Reactions of aluminium

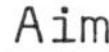

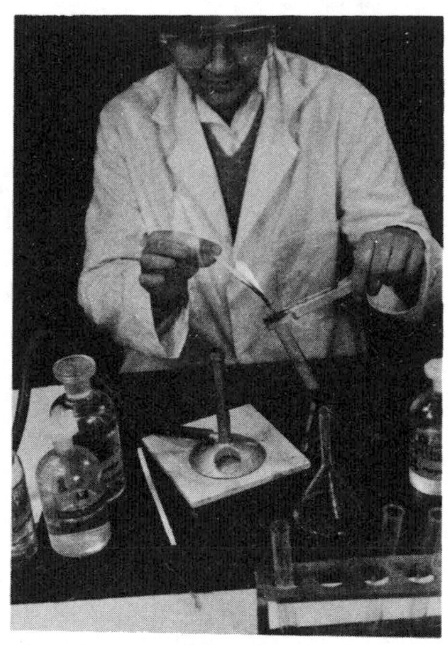

Aim

The purpose of this experiment is to show how aluminium foil reacts with dilute acids and alkalis and, when reactions do occur, to carry out tests on the resulting solutions.

Introduction

In Unit I3 (The Periodic Table) you learned that aluminium oxide is amphoteric. Other metals with amphoteric oxides such as beryllium and zinc tend to react with acids and alkalis, so you might also expect aluminium to react in a similar way.

In addition to observing the reactions of aluminium with dilute acids and alkalis, you also attempt to interpret some reactions of the resulting solutions.

Requirements

safety spectacles
6 pieces of aluminium foil, 3 cm x 3 cm
10 test-tubes
test-tube rack
test-tube holder
sodium hydroxide solution, 2 M NaOH ------------------- 
hydrochloric acid, dilute, 2 M HCl
Bunsen burner and bench mat
beaker, 100 cm^3
copper(II) chloride solution, 0.1 M $CuCl_2$
mercury(II) chloride solution, 0.1 M $HgCl_2$ ---------------- 
wash-bottle of distilled water
filter funnel
filter paper
sulphuric acid, dilute, 1 M H_2SO_4
sodium carbonate solution, 1 M Na_2CO_3
red and blue litmus papers

Procedure

Reactions of aluminium foil

1. Tear one of the sheets of aluminium foil into smaller pieces and place them in a test-tube containing 3-4 cm^3 of dilute sodium hydroxide solution. Identify any gas given off and record your observations in a copy of Results Table 1. Keep the resulting solution for further tests.
2. Repeat step 1 using dilute hydrochloric acid instead of sodium hydroxide solution. If no reaction occurs, heat the mixture gently.

3. Place three pieces of aluminium in a small beaker and just cover them with copper(II) chloride solution. On a fourth piece of aluminium, place three separate drops of mercury(II) chloride solution.

4. After about two minutes, pour away the copper(II) chloride solution and rinse the foil with distilled water. Leave one piece exposed to the air. Put the others in two test-tubes and add sodium hydroxide and dilute hydrochloric acid respectively. Compare what happens with the results of steps 1 and 2.

5. Rinse away the drops of mercury(II) chloride solution with distilled water and leave the foil exposed to the air. Examine it after a few minutes and compare it with the foil treated with copper(II) chloride.

<u>Reactions of the resulting solutions</u>

6. Filter the resulting solutions from steps 1 and 2 (if necessary) and divide each solution into three portions.

7. To separate portions of the solutions, add the following reagents, a little at a time, until they are present in excess:

   (a) dilute sulphuric acid,

   (b) dilute sodium hydroxide solution,

   (c) sodium carbonate solution.

8. Record your observations in a copy of Results Table 2. If no reaction occurs write NONE in the appropriate box.

Results Table 1 Reactions of aluminium foil

Reagent	Observations	Identity of any gas given off
Sodium hydroxide solution		
Dilute hydrochloric acid		
Dilute hydrochloric acid [after $CuCl_2(aq)$]		
Air after immersion in $CuCl_2(aq)$		
Air after immersion in $HgCl_2(aq)$		

Results Table 2 Reactions of the solutions

	Observations using solutions of:	
Reagent	Al in NaOH	Al in HCl
Dilute sulphuric acid		
Sodium hydroxide solution		
Sodium carbonate solution		

(Specimen results on page 86)

You may need to refer to your textbook(s) in order to answer the following questions.

Questions

1. Untreated aluminium has a wide variety of uses which depend, in part, on its resistance to corrosion in normal conditions. However, standard electrode potentials suggest that aluminium is more reactive than iron, which corrodes badly. Explain briefly. (You study the uses of aluminium further in Level Two.)

2. How does treatment with a solution of copper(II) chloride or mercury(II) chloride reveal the true reactivity of aluminium?

3. Suggest a reason for the fact that mercury(II) chloride is more effective than copper(II) chloride in promoting a reaction between aluminium and air.

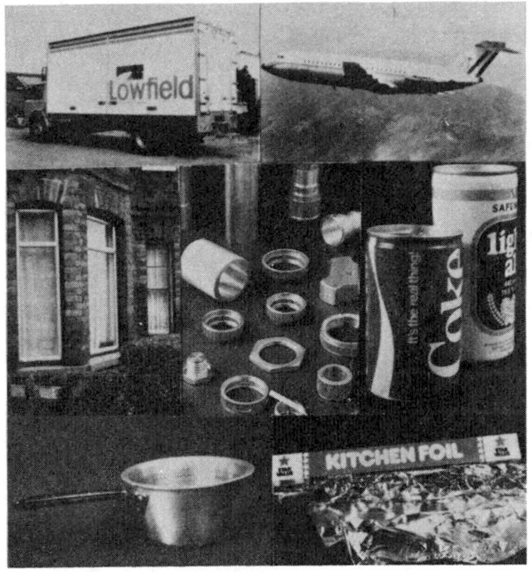

Fig.3. Some useful products made from aluminium

4. Why should you not use washing-soda or some special oven-cleaners on aluminium kitchenware?

5. Use the data in Exercise 3 to write equations for the reactions of aluminium with dilute acids and alkalis.

6. Explain, as far as possible, the observations you have made in Results Table 2 and name the precipitates formed. (Hint: aluminium carbonate is not known.)

(Answers on page 87)

Now attempt the next exercise, which is related to the experiment you have just done and also helps you to revise calculations based on the mole.

Exercise 4 (a) Suggest how the compound $Al_2(SO_4)_3 \cdot xH_2O$ could be prepared in crystalline form from aluminium.

(b) A hydrated aluminium sulphate, $Al_2(SO_4)_3 \cdot xH_2O$, contains 8.1% of aluminium by mass.

(i) calculate the value of x;

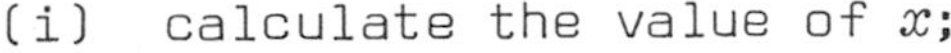

(ii) comment on the colour of an aqueous solution of the salt.

(c) The standard electrode potential for the couple $Al_3^+(aq)/Al(s)$ is -1.66 V. Why does aluminium not dissolve readily in dilute acids?

(Answers on page 87)

In Unit S4 (Bonding and Structure) you learned that there are compounds in which boron and aluminium atoms have fewer than eight electrons in their outer shells. We now consider some of these compounds, which are often described as being 'electron deficient'.

The halides of boron and aluminium

The halides of boron and aluminium may be prepared by direct combination you have already prepared aluminium chloride by this method in Unit I3 (The Periodic Table). In this section you build upon the knowledge of these compounds you have gained from Units I3 and S4 (Bonding and Structure).

Objectives. When you have finished this section, you should be able to:

(5) describe the bonding and structure of the fluorides and chlorides of boron and aluminium;

(6) describe the hydrolysis of the chlorides of boron and aluminium;

(7) explain the acidic nature of solutions of boric(III) acid, $B(OH)_3$, and aluminium salts.

In the next exercise you consider the bonding in some of the halides.

Exercise 5 (a) Look up and record the boiling-points of the fluorides and chlorides of boron and aluminium.

(b) Which of the above halides has the greatest ionic character? Explain your answer.

(c) Place the aluminium halides in order of decreasing ionic character and explain your answer in terms of polarizability of the anion.

(Answers on page 87)

In Unit S4 (Bonding and Structure) you learned how to predict the shapes of molecules and recognise ionic and covalent substances. In the next exercise you apply this knowledge to the chlorides of boron and aluminium.

Exercise 6 (a) Draw a diagram of the BCl_3 molecule, indicating the shape and bond angles.

(b) Would you expect the chlorides of boron and aluminium to dissolve in organic solvents? Explain your answer.

(c) With the aid of diagrams and equations, explain the following facts.

(i) The relative molecular mass (M_r) of aluminium chloride vapour below 400 °C is 267.0 whereas at 800 °C it is 133.5.

(ii) At 600 °C, M_r for aluminium chloride vapour is between 267.0 and 133.5.

(d) Explain why M_r for boron chloride vapour does not appreciably exceed 117. (Hint: consider the small size of the boron atom.)

(Answers on page 88)

You learned in Unit I3 that the chlorides of boron and aluminium are hydrolysed by water. The same is true of the bromides and iodides, but not the fluorides. The next exercise concerns the hydrolysis of the chlorides of boron and aluminium. You may need to refer to your textbooks for some of the details.

Exercise 7 Study the following equations for hydrolysis reactions:

$BCl_3(l) + 3H_2O(l) \rightarrow B(OH)_3(aq) + 3HCl(aq)$

$AlCl_3(s) + 6H_2O(l) \rightarrow [Al(H_2O)_6]^{3+}(aq) + 3Cl^-(aq)$

(a) Copy the above equations and name the products formed in each reaction.

(b) Are the resulting solutions acidic, basic or neutral?

(c) Suggest a reason for the fact that the chloride of the top element in Group IV, CCl_4, does not hydrolyse whereas BCl_3 does.

(d) Sketch the shape of the complex ion $[Al(H_2O)_6]^{3+}$.

(e) Why does boron not form 6 co-ordinate complexes like the one you have just described?

(f) What alternative molecular formula is often used for $B(OH)_3$?

(Answers on page 88)

The last exercise suggests that $B(OH)_3(aq)$ and $[Al(H_2O_6]^{3+}$ behave as acids. In Unit I5 (Transition Elements) you learned that aqua complexes are often acidic, especially when the metal ions are small and highly charged. If necessary, refer back to the section on acidity of complex ions in Unit I5 to help you with the next exercise.

Exercise 8 In aqueous solution, $B(OH)_3$ forms hydronium (oxonium) ions as represented by the following equation:

$B(OH)_3(aq) + 2H_2O(l) \rightarrow [B(OH)_4]^-(aq) + H_3O^+(aq)$

(a) Write equations to show the formation of hydronium ions by $[Al(H_2O)_6]^{3+}$.

(b) Look up and record values of K_a for the species $B(OH)_3$ and $[Al(H_2O)_6]^{3+}$. Which is the stronger acid?

(c) Explain why $B(OH)_3$ reacts with a water molecule to form $[B(OH)_4]^-(aq)$.

(d) The dissociation of the hydrated aluminium(III) ion suggests that the O—H bond in the coordinated water molecule is weakened so that an adjacent uncoordinated water molecule can more readily accept a proton from it. Why do you think this might happen?

(e) Why is the transfer of a proton from $[Al(H_2O)_5(OH)]^{2+}$ less likely than from $[Al(H_2O)_6]^{3+}$ in aqueous solution?

(Answers on page 88)

The next exercise investigates the conditions under which three or more protons can be transferred from $[Al(H_2O)_6]^{3+}$. It is related to Experiment 1.

Exercise 9 In the hydrolysis of the hexaaquaaluminium(III) ion $[Al(H_2O)_6]^{3+}$, the water behaves as a weak base. The product of hydrolysis depends on the strength of the base. With this in mind, interpret the following observations:

(a) When sodium carbonate solution is added to $[Al(H_2O)_6]^{3+}$ a white precipitate forms.

(b) When sodium hydroxide solution is added to $[Al(H_2O)_6]^{3+}$ a white precipitate forms initially but this re-dissolves in excess sodium hydroxide solution.

(Answers on page 88)

In the following Teacher-marked Exercise you compare the acidity of solutions of aluminium ions and other metal ions. It would be instructive to include sodium ions (radius 0.095 nm) in your discussion.

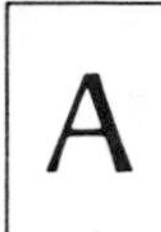

Teacher-marked Exercise Discuss the relative acidity of solutions of $AlCl_3$, $FeCl_2$ and $FeCl_3$, given the ionic radii Al^{3+}, 0.050 nm; Fe^{2+}, 0.076 nm; Fe^{3+}, 0.065 nm.

The hexaaquaaluminium(III) ion yields a species having the general formula $[Al(H_2O)_x(OH)_y]^z$ when treated with a base. State and justify a simple algebraic expression connecting (i) x and y, (ii) y and z.

Show why the particular species obtained is related to the strength of the base added, using H_2O, CO_3^{2-}, and OH^- as examples of bases.

How are the foregoing principles related to the observations made when 2 M sodium hydroxide is added to solutions of (a) $AlCl_3$, (b) $FeCl_2$, (c) $FeCl_3$?

Having discussed the halides we now consider some Group II oxides.

The oxides of boron and aluminium

In Unit I3 (The Periodic Table) you learned that boron oxide is acidic and has a giant covalent structure whereas aluminium oxide is amphoteric and has a giant ionic structure. These properties are consistent with the change from non-metal in the case of boron to 'weak' metal in the case of aluminium. The word 'weak' is used because aluminium does not show all the typical chemical characteristics of metals.

Objectives. When you have finished this section you should be able to:

(8) write a chemical equation for the reaction between boron oxide and water;

(9) list some commercial uses of aluminium oxide;

(10) compare the stabilities of boron oxide and aluminium oxide.

The next exercise deals with boron oxide. This question uses the following data about boron and its compounds. On the graph the number of electrons removed is plotted against the logarithm of the appropriate ionization energy and, in the table, standard enthalpy changes are listed for various processes.

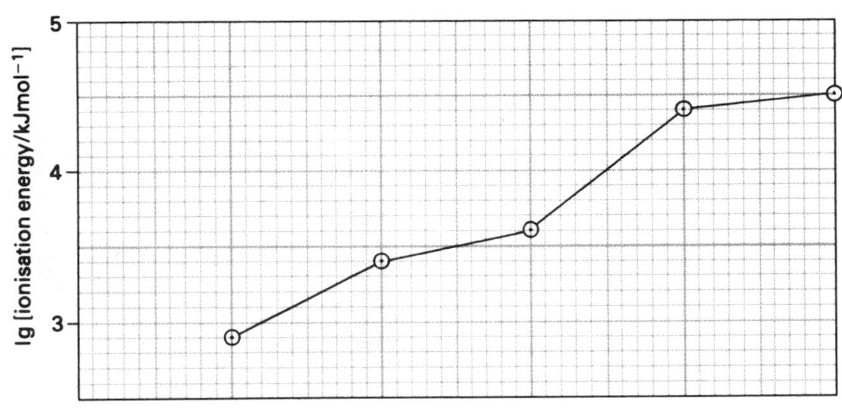

Fig.4.

Table 1

Process	$\Delta H^{\ominus}$(298 K)/kJ mol^{-1}
First electron affinity of oxygen	-140
Second electron affinity of oxygen	+790
Standard heat of atomization of oxygen	+250
Standard heat of atomization of boron	+590
Standard heat of formation of the oxide of boron	-1270
First ionization energy of boron	+800
Second ionization energy of boron	+2400
Third ionization energy of boron	+3700
Fourth ionization energy of boron	+25000
Fifth ionization energy of boron	+32800

Exercise 10 (a) On (a copy of) the graph, label each point with the electronic configuration (*s*, *p*, *d* or *f*) of the corresponding electron. Deduce the most likely formula for the oxide of boron.

(b) Draw a labelled Born-Haber cycle for the formation of the oxide of boron (assumed to be ionic). Calculate a lattice energy for the oxide of boron.

(c) One mole of the oxide of boron reacts with three moles of water and the product dissolves in water to give a weakly acidic solution. Write an equation, with state symbols, for the equilibrium occurring in aqueous solution.

(d) Would you expect your value for the lattice energy of the oxide of boron to be in good or poor agreement with a theoretically derived value? Give your reason(s).

(Answers on page 89)

In the next exercise you compare the stabilities of aluminium oxide and boron oxide. You need not use $\Delta G^\ominus$ values if you have not studied them before.

Exercise 11 (a) Write down the values of $\Delta H_f^\ominus$ and/or $\Delta G_f^\ominus$ for B_2O_3 and Al_2O_3, using your data book.

(b) Which of the oxides is the more stable? Explain your answer.

(Answers on page 89)

In Unit S3 (Chemical Energetics) you learned that aluminium will reduce iron(III) oxide to iron and form aluminium oxide (thermit process). This process makes use of the high negative enthalpy of formation of aluminium oxide.

Fig.5. Thermit SkV-F process.

Read about the uses of aluminium oxide in your textbook(s) so that you can do the following exercise. We suggest that you leave till Level Two a study of the process known as anodizing, which thickens the protective layer of oxide on the surface of aluminium.

Exercise 12 List three important uses of aluminium oxide.

(Answer on page 89)

Aluminium sulphate and potassium aluminium sulphate

Objectives. When you have finished this section you should be able to:

(11) state the effect of heat on aluminium sulphate;

(12) describe the preparation of potassium aluminium sulphate (potash alum);

(13) state the general formula of alums;

(14) describe how potassium aluminium sulphate reacts with dilute sodium hydroxide, barium chloride solution and sodium carbonate solution;

(15) list some uses of aluminium sulphate.

Read about the preparation of potassium aluminium sulphate, its properties, uses and formula. You should also read about the properties and uses of aluminium sulphate and compare it with potassium aluminium sulphate. This will help you with the two exercises which follow.

Fig.6.

Exercise 13 (a) Write an equation to show the thermal decomposition of aluminium sulphate.

(b) Suggest a reason, in terms of the polarizing effect of Al^{3+}, for the relative ease of decomposition of aluminium sulphate compared to other sulphates.

(c) State three uses of aluminium sulphate.

(Answers on page 89)

Exercise 14 (a) Briefly describe how crystals of potassium aluminium sulphate can be made from potassium sulphate and aluminium sulphate.

(b) State the general formula of the alums and give the formula of potassium aluminium sulphate.

(c) Would you expect a solution of potassium aluminium sulphate to be neutral, acidic or basic? Explain.

(Answers on page 90)

In the next exercise you compare the reactions of aluminium sulphate and potassium aluminium sulphate. You may find it useful to consult a textbook of inorganic qualitative analysis.

Exercise 15 (a) Complete a copy of Table 2.

Table 2

Test	Observations	Equations
1. Flame test (i) $Al_2(SO_4)_3$ (ii) $KAl(SO_4)_2$		
2. Dropwise addition of excess NaOH(aq) (i) $Al_2(SO_4)_3(aq)$ (ii) $KAl(SO_4)_2(aq)$		
3. Addition of $Na_2CO_3(aq)$ (i) $Al_2(SO_4)_3(aq)$ (ii) $KAl(SO_4)_2(aq)$		
4. Addition of $BaCl_2(aq)$ (i) $Al_2(SO_4)_3(aq)$ (ii) $KAl(SO_4)_2(aq)$		

(b) What is the difference between a double salt and a complex salt? In which category are the alums?

(Answers on page 90)

In order to consolidate your knowledge of Group III elements, attempt the following Teacher-marked Exercise. Don't forget to plan your answer before you start writing.

Teacher-marked Exercise

(a) Give an account of the similarities and differences between boron and aluminium, illustrating your answer with references to:

  (i) the physical properties of the elements,

  (ii) the stabilities and acid-base nature of the oxides,

  (iii) the bonding and structure of the halides,

  (iv) the hydrolysis of the chlorides.

(b) Give one illustration in each case of the diagonal relationship of boron and aluminium with elements in neighbouring groups.

(c) Suggest two important ways in which you would expect thallium compounds to differ from boron compounds.

Apart from some industrial aspects, which you consider in Level Two, you have now completed a study of Group III elements. Ask your teacher how much of the next section, which concerns Group V, is relevant to your syllabus.

GROUP V: NITROGEN AND PHOSPHORUS

By now, you have come to expect considerable differences between the first and second members of a group in the Periodic Table. In Group V, the contrast appears to be very great since nitrogen is a colourless, unreactive gas while phosphorus, especially in its white form, is a very reactive solid. However, you will find that the usual group trends and similarities are also evident, particularly in the compounds.

Nitrogen constitutes four-fifths of the earth's atmosphere and it also occurs in chemical combination, mainly as nitrates. It is an essential element to living matter, being an important constituent of proteins and nucleic acids. Although white phosphorus is toxic, phosphorus compounds are necessary for life processes; the remaining elements in the group, especially arsenic, are toxic in elemental or combined forms towards most living organisms.

The nature of the elements

Objectives. When you have finished this section you should be able to:

(16) describe the structures of the red and white allotropes (polymorphs) of phosphorus;

(17) explain why nitrogen is a fairly unreactive gas while phosphorus is a reactive solid;

(18) describe the reactions of nitrogen and phosphorus with (a) hydrogen, (b) oxygen, (c) chlorine, (d) selected metals, (e) alkali, and (f) concentrated nitric acid.

Read the introduction to Group V in your textbooks, paying particular attention to the allotropes of phosphorus and their structure, and to the chemical reactions of nitrogen and phosphorus. Use the information you find to help you with the following exercises.

Exercise 16

(a) Write the electronic configurations of nitrogen and phosphorus atoms using the *s*, *p*, *d* notation. How many outer-shell electrons are there in all Group V elements?

(b) Draw a dot-and-cross diagram to show the bonding in the N_2 molecule.

(c) Name three allotropes of phosphorus and describe their appearance.

(d) Draw diagrams showing how the phosphorus atoms are linked in red and white phosphorus. Which has the higher boiling-point?

(e) How may red phosphorus be converted into white phosphorus?

(f) Bearing in mind the usual group trends, what would you expect to be the structure of bismuth?

(Answers on page 90)

In the next exercise you are asked to make some predictions about ion formation in Group V from your knowledge of other groups in the Periodic Table.

Exercise 17 (a) Generally speaking, the compounds of all Group V elements have considerable covalent character. Which of the elements (if any) are most likely to form the following ions (X denotes any Group V element)?

(i) X^{5-} (ii) X^{3-} (iii) X^{3+}

(b) Name one compound which contains the X^{3-} ion and one which contains the X^{3+} ion.

(Answers on page 90)

The next exercise concerns a practical situation. You should not attempt the experiment, because it is potentially dangerous.

Exercise 18 A few pieces of white phosphorus heated with a solution of sodium hydroxide produce a colourless gas called phosphine, PH_3. The apparatus shown in Fig. 7 below can be used to carry out this reaction but, before heating, it is necessary to pass a slow stream of nitrogen through the apparatus for a few minutes.

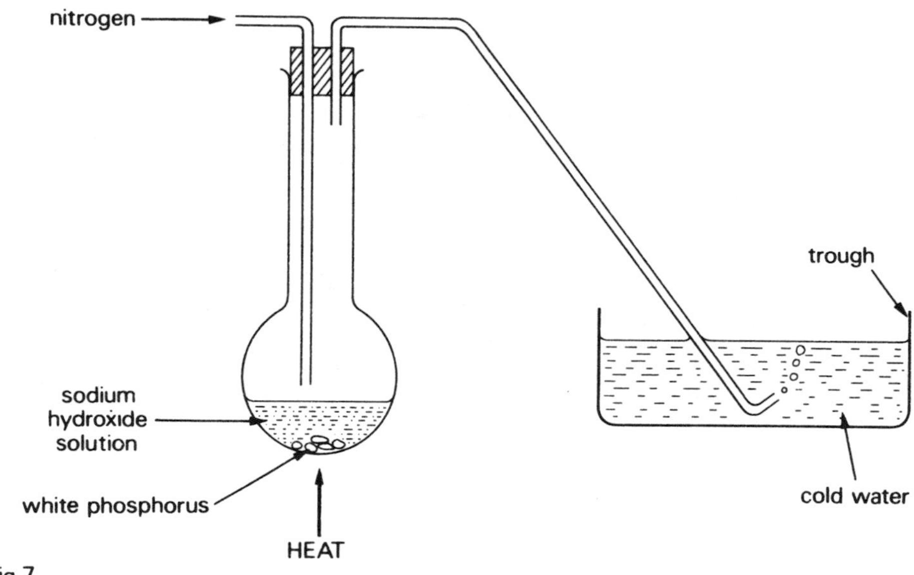

Fig. 7.

Phosphine has an objectionable odour, is highly poisonous and is spontaneously flammable when in contact with air. It is only very slightly soluble in water and has no effect on moist pH paper.

(a) Explain why it is necessary to pass nitrogen through the apparatus before heating the flask.

(b) What would you expect to happen when the phosphine gas bubbles reach the surface of the water in the trough?

(c) Describe how you would collect a sample of the phosphine gas prepared in this way.

(Answers on page 90)

Exercise 19 (a) Complete a larger copy of Table 3 which summarises the reactions of nitrogen and phosphorus.

Table 3

Reagent	Nitrogen	White phosphorus	Red phosphorus
Hydrogen		No reaction	No reaction
Oxygen			Ignites at 260 °C → P_4O_6 or P_4O_{10}
Chlorine	No reaction		
Magnesium			
Alkali	No reaction		No reaction
Conc. HNO_3	No reaction		

(b) Write equations for the reactions between white phosphorus and

(i) sodium hydroxide solution,

(ii) magnesium.

(c) State one chemical and one physical difference (in addition to colour) between red and white phosphorus.

(d) What is the reason for the differences in (c)?

(Answers on page 91)

In the last exercise you saw that nitrogen is fairly unreactive while phosphorus, especially the white allotrope, is very reactive. (We deal with the exception to this general rule, namely the reactivity towards hydrogen, later in this Unit.)

In the next exercise you investigate the reasons why phosphorus is generally more reactive than nitrogen.

Exercise 20 Fig. 8 shows some bond energy terms for Group V elements. Use the data to answer the questions which follow.

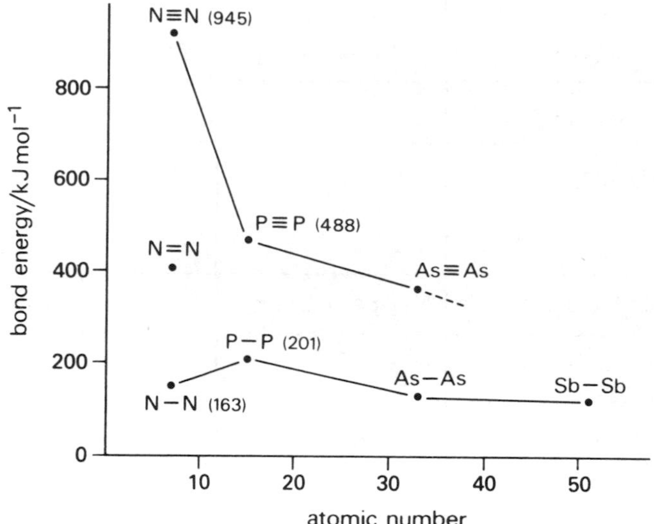

Fig. 8.

(a) State the type and number of bonds in a P_4 molecule. (Refer to Exercise 16, if necessary.)

(b) Calculate $\Delta H^{\ominus}$ for the following processes:

(i) $4P(g) \rightarrow P_4(g)$

(ii) $4N(g) \rightarrow N_4(g)$

(iii) $4P(g) \rightarrow 2P{\equiv}P(g)$

(iv) $4N(g) \rightarrow 2N{\equiv}N(g)$

(c) In view of your answer to (b), suggest why nitrogen forms diatomic molecules whereas P, As and Sb in the vapour state all exist as X_4 molecules.

(d) Why do you think the N≡N bond is so much stronger than the P≡P bond? (Hint: Consider how multiple bonds are formed by the overlap of atomic orbitals.)

(e) Suggest a reason why nitrogen is less reactive than phosphorus.

(Answers on page 91)

With the above exercise in mind attempt the next exercise, which is part of an A-level question.

Exercise 21 Consider the structures of molecular nitrogen and phosphorus and attempt to explain the relative affinities of these two elements towards (i) oxygen, (ii) chlorine.

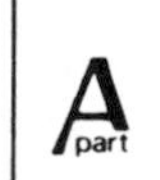

(Answer on page 91)

The next exercise is an A-level question which deals with the reaction of white phosphorus with copper(II) sulphate solution.

Exercise 22 White phosphorus reacts with dilute aqueous solutions of copper(II) sulphate to deposit metallic copper and produce a strongly acidic solution.

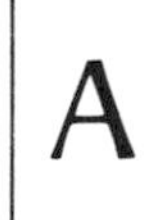

In an experiment to investigate this reaction, 0.31 g of white phosphorus reacted in excess aqueous copper(II) sulphate giving 1.60 g of metallic copper.

(P = 31, Cu = 64)

(a) (i) Calculate the number of moles of phosphorus atoms used.

(ii) Calculate the number of moles of copper produced.

(iii) Hence calculate the number of moles of copper deposited by one mole of phosphorus atoms.

(b) (i) State the change in oxidation number of the copper in this reaction.

(ii) Calculate the new oxidation number of the phosphorus after the reaction.

(iii) In the reaction the phosphorus forms an acid, HPO_n. What is the value of n?

(c) Now write a balanced equation showing the action of white phosphorus on copper(II) sulphate in the presence of water.

(d) (i) In performing this experiment, what practical difficulty would you expect in weighing the piece of phosphorus?

(ii) Describe how you would try to overcome this difficulty.

(Answers on page 92)

We now consider in more detail some of the compounds of nitrogen and phosphorus that have been mentioned in your study of the elements, where you have already noticed the existence of several different oxidation states. This is most evident for nitrogen, largely due to the variety of oxides, but there is only one chloride of nitrogen, as you see in the next section.

Halides of nitrogen and phosphorus

Objectives. When you have finished this section you should be able to:

(19) explain why nitrogen forms only one chloride whereas phosphorus forms two;

(20) describe and explain the hydrolysis of NCl_3 and PCl_3;

(21) describe the hydrolysis of PCl_5 and the chlorides of the other elements in Group V.

Read about the chlorides of nitrogen and phosphorus, paying particular attention to their structures, their stability and their reactions with water. You should then be able to do the following exercises.

Exercise 23 Study the energy level diagrams in Fig. 9 and answer the questions which follow.

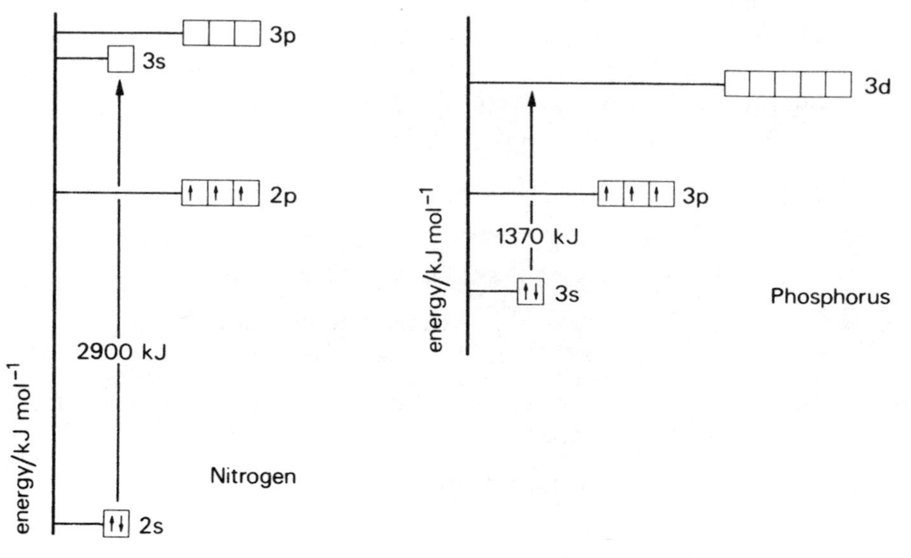

Fig. 9. Energy level diagrams for nitrogen and phosphorus.

(a) Explain why phosphorus can form two chlorides, PCl_3 and PCl_5, whereas nitrogen has only one, NCl_3.

(b) Phosphorus pentachloride has a molecular structure in the liquid state, but the solid is ionic. Write the formulae of the two ions.

(Answers on page 92)

Exercise 24 (a) Using your data book, record values of $\Delta H^{\ominus}_{f}$ for $NCl_3(l)$ and $PCl_3(l)$.

(b) Write the relevant thermochemical equations for (a).

(c) What do the values in (a) suggest about the stability of these compounds? Is this borne out by their known properties?

(Answers on page 92)

In Unit I3 (The Periodic Table) you learned that the trichlorides, NCl_3 and PCl_3, are hydrolysed by water. In the next exercise you remind yourselves of these reactions and extend your knowledge to the hydrolysis of the pentachloride, PCl_5.

Exercise 25 Write equations and name the products for the reactions of NCl_3, PCl_3 and PCl_5 with water.

(Answers on page 92)

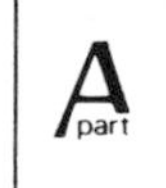

The different products obtained when NCl_3 and PCl_3 are hydrolysed suggest that different mechanisms operate in these reactions. You explore this idea in the next exercise.

Exercise 26 The first step in the hydrolysis of phosphorus trichloride is the substitution of an —OH group for —Cl.

(a) Suggest a mechanism for this substitution (addition-elimination) via the intermediate:

```
       Cl
       |      H
       |     /
  Cl — P ← O
       |     \
       |      H
       Cl
```

(b) Two similar steps follow, in which the other two chlorine atoms are replaced by hydroxy groups. Show how the product of these two steps, $P(OH)_3$, rearranges to give phosphonic acid (phosphorous acid).

(c) Why can the hydrolysis of nitrogen trichloride not proceed by a similar mechanism?

(d) Insert arrows showing electron shifts to complete the following suggested mechanism for the first step in the hydrolysis of nitrogen trichloride.

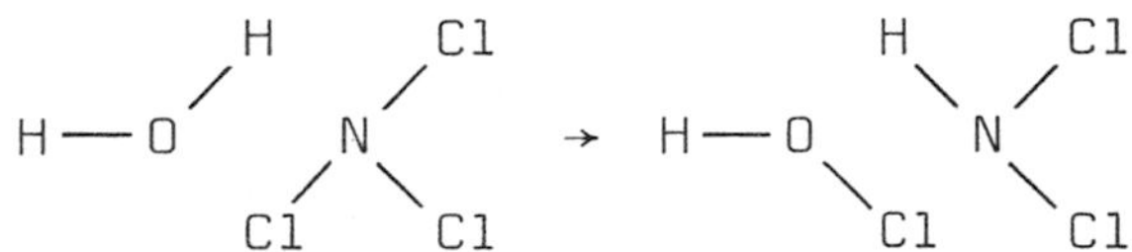

Two similar steps follow, giving NH_3 and $3HClO$ as the final products.

(Answers on page 92)

As Group V is descended, hydrolysis of the trichloride becomes less complete. In the next exercise you investigate the hydrolysis of antimony and bismuth trichlorides.

Exercise 27 The hydrolysis of antimony trichloride is given by the following equation.

$$SbCl_3(aq) + H_2O(l) \rightleftharpoons SbClO(s) + 2HCl(aq)$$

white ppt.
antimony(III) chloride oxide

(a) What would you observe if concentrated hydrochloric acid is added to the equilibrium mixture above?

(b) How would you expect bismuth trichloride to react with water? Give a balanced equation.

(c) Why do laboratory solutions of antimony and bismuth trichlorides contain added hydrochloric acid?

(Answers on page 93)

Apart from the tri- and pentahalides mentioned above, nitrogen forms a fluoride where the nitrogen is in an oxidation state of +1. The compound dinitrogen difluoride, N_2F_2, exhibits an interesting form of isomerism which we consider in the next exercise.

Exercise 28 (a) Draw a dot-and-cross diagram for the molecule N_2F_2. (Hint: it contains a double bond.)

A

(b) What type of isomerism is exhibited by N_2F_2? Draw diagrams showing the arrangement of the atoms in the isomers. Name these isomers and indicate briefly what structural feature is responsible for their existence.

(Answers on page **93**)

Now we turn to another group of compounds, in which five different oxidation states are found.

The oxides of nitrogen and phosphorus

Objectives. When you have finished this section, you should be able to:

(22) place the common oxides of (a) nitrogen and (b) phosphorus in order of increasing stability;

(23) outline the preparation of NO, NO_2, N_2O_4, P_4O_6 and P_4O_{10};

(24) explain the meaning of the term odd-electron molecule and draw dot-and-cross diagrams for NO, NO_2 and N_2O_4;

(25) draw the structures of P_4O_6 and P_4O_{10}.

Table 4, which is incomplete, summarises some information about the oxides of nitrogen and phosphorus. You complete it in the next exercise.

Table 4

Oxidation state of N or P		+1	+2	+3	+4	+5
Nitrogen oxides	Formula	N_2O			NO_2, N_2O_4	
	Common name	Nitrous oxide	Nitric oxide	Nitrogen trioxide		
	Recommended name	Dinitrogen oxide		Dinitrogen trioxide		
	$\Delta H_f^{\ominus}$ ($\Delta G_f^{\ominus}$) /kJ mol^{-1}			+84 (+139)		
Phosphorus oxides	Formula			P_4O_6	P_4O_8	P_4O_{10}
	Common name				Rarely met	
	Recommended name				Phosphorus (IV) oxide	
	$\Delta H_f^{\ominus}$ ($\Delta G_f^{\ominus}$) /kJ mol^{-1}			-1640.1 (—)		

Exercise 29 (a) Complete a larger copy of Table 4.

(b) Place the oxides of nitrogen in order of increasing thermal stability under standard conditions.

(c) In view of the fact that the common oxidation states of Group V are +3 and +5, is your answer to part (b) surprising?

(d) Which of the common oxides of phosphorus is the more stable?

(Answers on page 93)

Read about the appearance, structure and laboratory preparation of NO, NO_2, N_2O_4, P_4O_6 and P_4O_{10} so that you can do the following two exercises.

Exercise 30 (a) Describe the appearance of the following:

(i) NO at room temperature,

(ii) NO_2 at about 30 °C,

(iii) N_2O_4 at about 5 °C.

(b) Describe briefly, giving reagents, reaction conditions and equations, how NO, NO_2 and N_2O_4 could be conveniently prepared from nitric acid.

Comment on the method of collection of NO.

(c) Describe and explain what happens to N_2O_4 when it is heated from -10 °C to 600 °C.

(Answers on page 94)

Exercise 31 (a) Briefly outline the preparation of P_4O_6 and P_4O_{10} from white phosphorus.

(b) Sketch the structures of P_4O_6 and P_4O_{10} from Fig. 10 below.

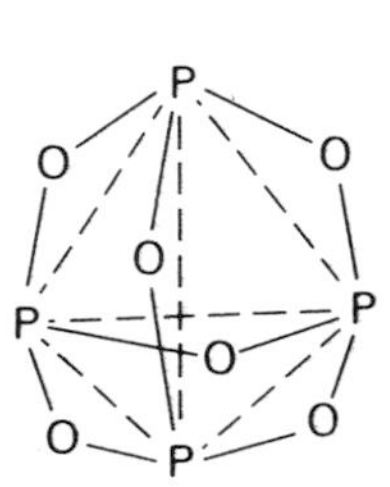

P_4O_6

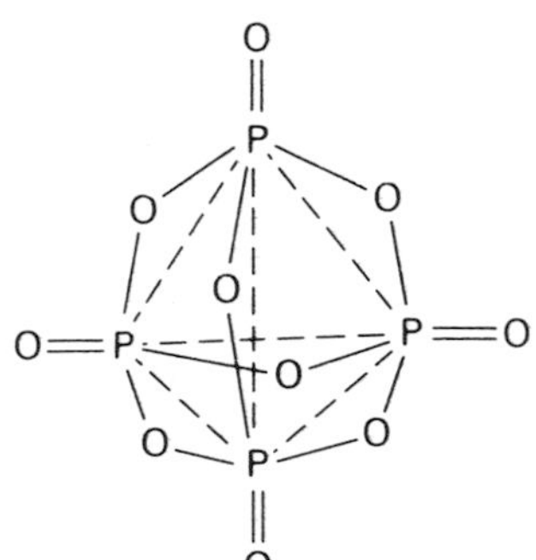

P_4O_{10}

Fig.10.

How are the structures of the molecules P_4, P_4O_6 and P_4O_{10} related to each other?

(c) Phosphorus(III) oxide catches fire on heating in air. What product is formed? Write an equation.

(Answers on page 94)

The structures of the oxides of phosphorus, as you have seen, can be represented simply by the allocation of outer-shell electrons to bonding pairs and non-bonding pairs (lone pairs). Molecules of some of the oxides of nitrogen, however, have an odd number of outer-shell electrons, at least one of which remains unpaired. For this reason, they are often referred to as 'odd-electron' molecules.

Odd-electron molecules

In the next exercise you investigate which of the nitrogen oxides contain unpaired electrons.

Exercise 32 With the aid of diagrams, give the electronic structures of NO, NO_2 and N_2O_4.

Comment on any unusual features.

(Answers on page 94)

Odd-electron molecules tend to react in a way that will remove the unpaired electron, either by losing it (oxidation) or by pairing it with an unpaired electron in another molecule. With this in mind, attempt the next exercise.

Exercise 33

(a) Why does NO_2 form a dimer?

(b) Would you expect NO to form a dimer? Explain your answer.

(c) How would you expect NO to react with chlorine?

(d) You have encountered ions with unpaired electrons in Unit I5 (Transition Elements). What properties associated with these ions might you also expect for odd-electron molecules?

(e) What cations might be formed from NO and NO_2?

(Answers on page 95)

We now go on to consider some of the reactions of the oxides.

Chemical reactions of the oxides of nitrogen and phosphorus

Objectives. When you have finished this section you should be able to:

(26) compare the reactions of the oxides N_2O, NO and NO_2 with (a) chlorine, (b) metals, (c) iron(II) ions and (d) water;

(27) state and explain the effect of dinitrogen oxide, N_2O, on a glowing splint;

(28) describe the hydrolysis of the oxides of phosphorus.

Read about the chemical properties of the oxides of nitrogen and and phosphorus so that you can do the following exercises. Table 5, which is incomplete, gives you some guidance.

Table 5

Reactant	N_2O	NO	NO_2
Cl_2	No reaction		NO_2 oxidized to HNO_3 if moist.
Metal, e.g. Cu or Fe		NO reduced to N_2 by red-hot metal.	NO_2 reduced to N_2 (possibly via NO) by hot metal.
$Fe^{2+}(aq)$	No reaction		Fe^{2+} oxidized to Fe^{3+}.
Glowing splint		No reaction.	
H_2O			

Exercise 34

(a) Complete a larger copy of Table 5 to summarise the properties of the three oxides N_2O, NO and NO_2.

(b) Place the three oxides in order of increasing oxidizing ability.

(c) Which of the oxides is commonly known as 'laughing gas'?

(d) Which of the products considered in the Table forms the basis of the brown ring test for nitrates?

(e) Use the information below to answer the question.

Half-reaction	$E^{\ominus}/V$
1. $NO_3^-(aq) + 2H^+(aq) + e^- \rightleftharpoons NO_2(g) + H_2O(l)$	+0.80
2. $NO_3^-(aq) + 4H^+(aq) + 3e^- \rightleftharpoons NO(g) + 2H_2O(l)$	+0.96
3. $MnO_4^-(aq) + 8H^+(aq) + 5e^- \rightleftharpoons Mn^{2+}(aq) + 4H_2O(l)$	+1.51

What would you expect to observe when NO_2 and NO are bubbled through separate samples of acidified $KMnO_4$? Explain your answer and deduce balanced equations for the reactions.

(f) Why does a glowing wooden splint relight when placed in N_2O?

(g) Write equations for the reactions mentioned in Table 5.

(Answers on page 95)

Fig.11. Dinitrogen oxide is used as an anaesthetic in dentistry

Exercise 35

(a) Write chemical equations for the reactions of the oxides of phosphorus with water.

(b) Which of the oxides, P_4O_6 or P_4O_{10}, is hydrolysed more readily?

(c) State two laboratory uses of phosphorus(V) oxide.

(d) Predict the change in acid-base character of the oxides in the +3 oxidation state as the group is descended. Explain your answer.

(Answers on page **96**)

The oxides of arsenic and antimony in the +5 oxidation state are known but they are unstable with respect to the +3 states. Both of these oxides are acidic. Bismuth(V) oxide has never been obtained in the pure form.

You have seen that the oxides of phosphorus, and some of those of nitrogen, are the anhydrides of some well-known acids. We now consider those acids in more detail.

The oxoacids of nitrogen and phosphorus, and their salts

Although nitrogen forms five oxides, it forms only two important oxoacids; nitrous acid, HNO_2, and nitric acid, HNO_3. Phosphorus, on the other hand, forms fewer oxides than nitrogen but many more oxoacids. In this section we will deal only with the commonest oxoacid of phosphorus, phosphoric(V) acid, H_3PO_4.

Objectives. When you have finished this section you should be able to:

(29) give examples of oxidizing reactions of nitric acid and nitrous acid;

(30) identify reactions in which nitrous acid and nitrites behave as reducing agents;

(31) explain the unstable nature of nitrous acid;

(32) draw the shapes of H_3PO_4, PO_4^{3-}, HPO_4^{2-} and $H_2PO_4^-$;

(33) state some uses of phosphoric(V) acid and phosphates.

Read about the chemical properties of nitric acid, nitrous acid and phosphoric(V) acid in your textbook(s) to obtain an overall picture of these acids.

The next exercise is an A-level question which asks you to make predictions about nitrous acid, HNO_2.

Exercise 36 The information in this table may be used to predict the likely course of some reactions of nitrous acid, HNO_2:

Half-reaction			$E^\ominus$/V
$I_2(aq) + 2e^-$	$\rightleftharpoons$	$2I^-(aq)$	+0.54
$NO_3^-(aq) + 3H^+(aq) + 2e^-$	$\rightleftharpoons$	$HNO_2(aq) + H_2O(l)$	+0.94
$HNO_2(aq) + H^+(aq) + e^-$	$\rightleftharpoons$	$NO(g) + H_2O(l)$	+0.99
$Br_2(aq) + 2e^-$	$\rightleftharpoons$	$2Br^-(aq)$	+1.09

Nitrous acid is normally made freshly when it is required by adding ice-cold aqueous potassium nitrite (KNO_2) to dilute hydrochloric acid.

(a) (i) Explain why you would not expect nitrous acid to be stable.

(ii) Explain what the effect of a decrease of pH would be on the stability of nitrous acid.

(b) What are the likely products of reaction between nitrous acid and a solution containing iodine and iodide ions?

(c) What are the likely products of reaction between nitrous acid and a solution containing bromine and bromide ions?

(d) State the type of reactant that nitrous acid is in the reactions mentioned in (b) and (c).

(e) (i) State the likely products of the reaction between nitrous acid and a solution containing bromide ions and iodide ions.

(ii) What would you expect to SEE in the lower organic layer if the resulting mixture were shaken with a few drops of tetrachloromethane (carbon tetrachloride)?

(Answers on page 96)

Exercise 37 (a) Calculate the oxidation number of nitrogen in each of the following compounds:

HNO_3, HNO_2, NO_3^-, NO_2^-

(b) Do you think that nitric acid, nitrous acid and their salts could behave as both oxidizing and reducing agents?

(c) (i) Write a series of common nitrogen compounds in order of decreasing oxidation number to show the products you might expect in redox reactions involving nitric acid, nitrous acid and their salts.

(ii) How could you check whether your predictions were sensible before testing them by experiment?

(Answers on page 97)

In the following experiment you test some of the predictions you made in the preceding exercises.

EXPERIMENT 2

Reactions of the oxoacids of nitrogen and their salts

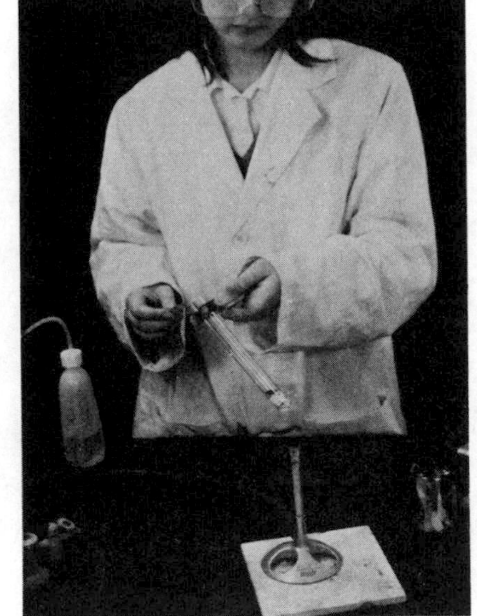

Aim and introduction

The purpose of this experiment is to illustrate some of the redox reactions of nitric acid, nitrates, nitrous acid and nitrites by means of simple small-scale tests.

Requirements

safety spectacles
protective gloves
6 test-tubes
copper turnings, Cu
nitric acid, concentrated, 16 M HNO_3
wash-bottle of distilled water
Bunsen burner and bench protection mat
magnesium ribbon, Mg
nitric acid, dilute, 2 M HNO_3
wood splints
2 boiling-tubes
sodium hydroxide solution, 2 M NaOH
Devarda's alloy (Cu 50%, Al 45%, Zn 5%)
aluminium foil, Al
sulphuric acid, dilute, 1 M H_2SO_4
beaker, 250 cm^3
ice
spatula
sodium nitrite, $NaNO_2$
potassium iodide solution, 0.5 M KI
potassium manganate(VII) solution, 0.2 M $KMnO_4$
iron(II) sulphate, $FeSO_4 \cdot 7H_2O$

Hazard warning

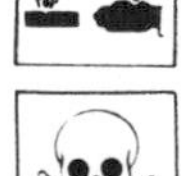

Concentrated nitric acid and aqueous sodium hydroxide are corrosive.

Nitrogen dioxide is a toxic gas which may be produced in reactions of nitrogen compounds.

Therefore you MUST:

WEAR SAFETY SPECTACLES AND PROTECTIVE GLOVES
WORK AT A FUME CUPBOARD

Procedure

A. Reactions of nitric acid

1. Place a single copper turning in a test-tube and carefully add a few drops of concentrated nitric acid. Record your observations in a copy of Results Table 2 and identify the gas evolved.

2. Pour about 2 cm^3 of concentrated nitric acid into a test-tube and carefully dilute it with an equal volume of distilled water. Drop in 2-3 copper turnings. Identify the gas evolved by observing its colour over the whole length of the test-tube. You may need to warm the tube gently to speed up the reaction.

3. Add about 4 cm^3 of 2 M nitric acid to a 4 cm piece of magnesium ribbon in a test-tube. Cork the tube loosely and attempt to identify the gas or gases evolved.

4. Add about 3 cm^3 of distilled water to a 4 cm piece of magnesium ribbon in a test-tube and add 1 cm^3 of 2 M nitric acid. Cork the tube loosely and attempt to identify the gas evolved.

5. In a boiling-tube, mix 1 cm^3 of 2 M nitric acid and 2 cm^3 of 2 M sodium hydroxide solution. Add a spatula measure of Devarda's alloy and warm gently. Identify the gas given off.

6. Repeat step 5 using a small piece of aluminium foil instead of Devarda's alloy. Complete your copy of Results Table 3.

B. Reactions of nitrous acid

7. Prepare a solution of nitrous acid, as follows. Pour about 15 cm^3 of dilute sulphuric acid into a boiling-tube and stand it in an ice-bath for about 5 minutes. Dissolve about 1.5 g of sodium nitrite in the minimum quantity of distilled water and cool in the ice-bath. Mix the two cooled solutions.

8. Transfer about 2 cm^3 of the nitrous acid solution to a test-tube and warm gently. Record your observations and try to identify the gas evolved.

9. In another test-tube add a few drops of potassium iodide solution to approximately 2 cm^3 of nitrous acid solution.

10. Repeat step 9 using a few drops of potassium manganate(VII) solution instead of potassium iodide.

11. Dissolve a few small crystals of iron(II) sulphate in about 2 cm^3 of cold distilled water.

    (a) To half of this solution add dilute aqueous sodium hydroxide.

    (b) Add the other half of the iron(II) sulphate solution to an equal volume of nitrous acid solution. Heat the mixture till the colour lightens and then cool. Add sodium hydroxide solution and compare the result with what happened in (a).

12. To a little solid sodium nitrite add 1-2 cm^3 of aqueous sodium hydroxide and a small piece of aluminium foil. Heat the mixture and test any gases evolved. Complete your copy of Results Table 4.

Results Table 2 Reactions of nitric acid and nitrates

Reactants	Observations	Identity of gas
1. Copper and 16 M HNO_3		
2. Copper and 8 M HNO_3		
3. Magnesium and 2 M HNO_3		
4. Magnesium and 0.5 M HNO_3		
5. Devarda's alloy and a nitrate in alkali		
6. Aluminium and a nitrate in alkali		

Results Table 3 Reactions of nitrous acid and nitrites

Reactants in solution	Observations	Identity of coloured product	Oxidation or reduction of NO_2^-
7. Sodium nitrite and sulphuric acid		HNO_2 or perhaps N_2O_3	-
8. Warm nitrous acid			
9. Potassium iodide and nitrous acid			
10. Potassium manganate(VII) and nitrous acid			
11a. Iron(II) sulphate and sodium hydroxide			
11b. Iron(II) sulphate, nitrous acid and sodium hydroxide			
12. Aluminium and a nitrite in alkali			

(Specimen results on page 97)

Questions

To help you with your answers you may need to refer to your text-books or to Exercises 36 and 37.

1. Write equations for the reactions between copper and nitric acid of different concentrations. Explain your observations of these reactions.
2. Describe and explain the difference between the reactions of magnesium with dilute and very dilute nitric acid.
3. Aluminium is the most powerful reducing agent of the three metals in Devarda's alloy. Suggest reasons why the alloy is more effective than aluminium foil.

4. Write an equation for the thermal decomposition of nitrous acid. What type of redox reaction is this? Why does nitric acid not undergo the same type of reaction?

5. Which of the reactions in the experiment may be used to distinguish:

   (a) nitrates and nitrites from most other compounds,

   (b) nitrates from nitrites?

(Answers on page 98)

The next exercise tests your understanding of the redox reactions of nitric acid.

Exercise 38 Under certain concentration and temperature conditions, 0.8 g of iron is found to react with 0.9 g of pure nitric acid, evolving an oxide of nitrogen (N_2O, or NO, or N_2O_4).

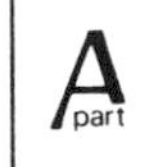

(a) Calculate the molar ratio of iron and nitric acid which react.

(b) Complete:

gain of ... electrons

$$\ldots Fe(s) + \ldots HNO_3(aq) \rightarrow \ldots Fe^{3+}(aq) + \left[\begin{array}{l} N_2O \\ \text{or } NO \\ \text{or } N_2O_4 \end{array}\right]$$

loss of ... electrons

(c) From the number of electrons gained by the nitric acid, deduce the change in oxidation number of nitrogen and decide which of the three oxides of nitrogen is formed.

(d) Complete:

$$\ldots Fe(s) - \ldots e^- \rightarrow \ldots Fe^{3+}(aq)$$

$$\ldots H^+ + 1HNO_3(aq) + \ldots e^- \rightarrow \left[\begin{array}{l} \tfrac{1}{2}N_2O \\ \text{or } 1NO \\ \text{or } \tfrac{1}{2}N_2O_4 \end{array}\right] + \ldots H_2O$$

and so, by addition, balance the equation for the reaction between iron and nitric acid under these conditions.

(H = 1; N = 14; O = 16; Fe = 56)

(Answers on page 98)

We deal with the industrial production and uses of nitric acid in Level Two of this Unit.

Now we consider the most important of the oxoacids of phosphorus - phosphoric(V) acid - and some of its salts.

Phosphoric(V) acid and phosphates

Phosphoric(V) acid, commonly called orthophosphoric acid, is a colourless solid when pure, but is more often seen as a syrupy liquid containing a small amount of water.

In the next exercise you build on what you have learned about phosphoric(V) acid in thè other ILPAC Units.

Exercise 39 (a) Write three equations to show the reactions that occur when an alkali is added to a solution of phosphoric(V) acid, H_3PO_4. Name the ions containing phosphorus.

(b) Would you expect a solution of trisodium phosphate, Na_3PO_4, to be acidic, alkaline or neutral? Explain briefly.

(c) The structural formula of phosphoric(V) acid can be represented as $PO(OH)_3$. What shape(s) would you expect for this molecule and for the ions formed from it?

(d) What type of intermolecular bonding would you expect to be predominant in phosphoric(V) acid in its solid and 'syrupy' states?

(e) Why is phosphoric(V) acid used in preference to sulphuric acid for the preparation of hydrogen bromide from a salt such as potassium bromide? Write an equation.

(f) Why is phosphoric(V) acid sometimes used in preference to sulphuric acid for the dehydration of organic molecules?

(Answers on page 98)

To help you with the following two exercises, read about the uses of phosphates, particularly in fertilizers, and the reactions of aqueous phosphate (orthophosphate) ions. You may find it useful to refer to a practical book dealing with inorganic qualitative analysis.

Exercise 40 (a) Complete a copy of Table 6.

Table 6. Some reactions of aqueous phosphates

Reagent in solution	Observations	Equation
Silver nitrate		$3Ag^+(aq) + PO_4^{3-}(aq) \rightarrow Ag_3PO_4(s)$
Barium chloride	White ppt.	
Iron(III) chloride		

(b) Describe, without writing an equation, how aqueous ammonium molybdate is used to confirm the presence of a phosphate(V) in solution.

(Answers on page 98)

Exercise 41 Phosphorus is essential for plant root growth and is one of the three most important elements (N, P, K) in artificial fertilizers. Compounds known as 'superphosphate' and 'triple-phosphate' are made from calcium phosphate(V), $Ca_3(PO_4)_2$, which is found naturally as 'rock phosphate'.

(a) Why is calcium phosphate not often used as a fertilizer?

(b) How is calcium phosphate converted to (i) 'superphosphate' and (ii) 'triple-phosphate' (triple-superphosphate)?

(c) What is the difference in chemical constitution between the superphosphate and the triple-phosphate?

(Answers on page 99)

Fig.12. Spreading phosphate fertilizer

We now turn our attention from the oxoacids of Group V elements to the hydrides.

The hydrides of nitrogen and phosphorus

Objectives. When you have finished this section you should be able to:

(34) list the hydrides formed by Group V elements;

(35) compare the shapes of the molecules of ammonia and phosphine;

(36) compare the boiling-points and the solubilities in water of ammonia and phosphine;

(37) state and explain the trend in the thermal stability of the tri-hydrides as the group is descended;

(38) explain the difference in base strength between ammonia and phosphine in aqueous solution;

(39) describe the effect of heat and of water on phosphonium iodide;

(40) compare the reducing and complexing properties of ammonia and phosphine.

All the Group V elements form tri-hydrides, XH_3. The stability of these hydrides falls rapidly down the group, so that SbH_3 and BiH_3 are very unstable, the latter having been obtained only in traces. Read about these hydrides to help you with the following exercises.

Exercise 42 Study Table 6 and answer the following questions about the hydrides of Group V.

Table 6

Element	Name and formula of hydride, XH_3	Other hydrides include:
Nitrogen	Ammonia, $NH_3(g)$	Hydrazine, $N_2H_4(l)$
Phosphorus	Phosphine, $PH_3(g)$	Diphosphane, $P_2H_4(l)$
Arsenic	Arsine, $AsH_3(g)$	
Antimony	Stibine, $SbH_3(g)$	
Bismuth	Bismuthine, $BiH_3(g)$	

(a) What are the oxidation numbers of the Group V elements in the hydrides listed in Table 6?

(b) Predict the shape of the PH_3 molecule from your knowledge of the shape of the NH_3 molecule.

(c) Suggest reasons why the bond angle in PH_3 is 93° compared to 107° in NH_3.

(Hint: consider the relative sizes and electronegativities of N and P.)

(d) An alternative explanation for the shape of the PH_3 molecule is that sp^3-hybridization does not occur as it does in NH_3, i.e. the lone pair is in the 3*s*-orbital and the bonding pairs are in 3*p*-orbitals. How does this account for the difference in bond angles?

(Answers on page **99**)

Exercise 43 (a) Write down the boiling-points of the first four hydrides, XH_3, in Group V. Use your data book.

(b) Comment on the trend in (a) and state the exception to the trend.

(c) Why is the boiling-point of ammonia higher than that of phosphine even though the relative molecular mass of phosphine is greater?

(Hint: consider the electronegativities of N, P and H.)

(d) Why do you think ammonia is soluble in water whereas phosphine is virtually insoluble?

(Answers on page **99**)

In the following exercise you consider the thermal stability of the XH_3 hydrides.

Exercise 44 (a) Ammonia is reasonably stable to heat, phosphine and arsine both decompose on heating and stibine and bismuthine are both unstable at room temperature.

Write equations to show the thermal decomposition of ammonia and phosphine.

(b) Complete a copy of Table 8 with the aid of your data book.

Table 8

Bond	Mean bond energy/kJ mol^{-1}
N—H	
P—H	
As—H	292
Sb—H	255
Bi—H	Not listed

(c) Do you think the bond energy terms listed in Table 7 are sufficient to explain the trend in thermal stability?

(Answers on page 99)

The presence of arsenic in food was once detected in forensic laboratories by the decomposition of arsine produced from the action of zinc and dilute acid on arsenic compounds. (See Fig. 13.)

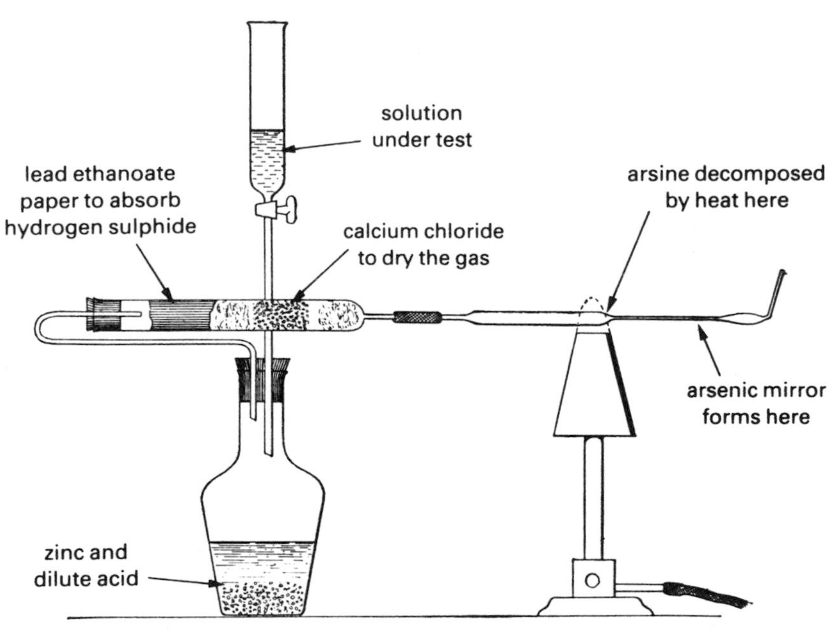

Fig.13. An old illustration of the apparatus used to detect arsenic in food.

In Unit 02 (Some Functional Groups) you compared the base strengths of ammonia and primary amines by considering the availability of the lone pairs of electrons on the nitrogen atoms and the relative stabilities of NH_4^+ and RNH_3^+. In the next exercise you similarly compare the base strength of ammonia with that of phospine.

Exercise 45 (a) Ammonia dissociates in water as follows:

$$NH_3(aq) + H_2O(l) \rightleftharpoons NH_4^+(aq) + OH^-(aq)$$

or $NH_3 \cdot H_2O(aq) \rightleftharpoons NH_4^+(aq) + OH^-(aq)$

The base dissociation constant, K_b(298 K), for this reaction is 1.77×10^{-5} mol dm^{-3}.

For a similar reaction involving the small amount of phosphine which dissolves, K_b is about 10^{-26} mol dm^{-3}.

Which is the more basic, phosphine or ammonia?

(b) Suggest a reason for the difference in base strength with reference to the orbital structures shown in Fig. 14 below:

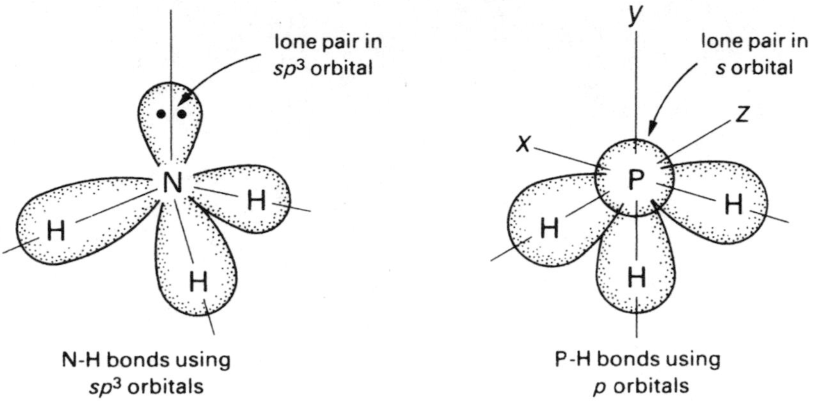

Fig.14.

(c) Would you expect the phosphonium ion, PH_4^+, to be more or less stable than NH_4^+. (Hint: look at your answer to (b) and at your copy of Table 7 in Exercise 44.)

(Answers on page 99)

Since water is a stronger base than phosphine, you might expect reactions to occur between phosphonium compounds and water similar to those which occur between ammonium compounds and dilute alkalis.

From your knowledge of ammonium compounds, attempt the next exercise which deals with phosphine and phosphonium (PH_4^+) compounds.

Exercise 46 (a) Write an equation for the reaction between phosphine and hydrogen chloride.

(b) Write an equation to show the effect of heat on phosphonium iodide.

(c) All phosphonium salts are immediately hydrolysed by water and dilute alkalis. Give two equations for this decomposition, one with water and the other with dilute sodium hydroxide.

(d) How do the reactions in (c) differ from the reactions with ammonium compounds?

(e) What is the shape of the phosphonium ion?

(Answers on page 99)

In Unit I5 (Transition Elements) and Unit I2 (The Halogens) you learned that ammonia can form complex ions with copper(II) and silver ions in solution. For the next exercise, find out from your textbook(s) whether phosphine behaves in a similar fashion.

Exercise 47 (a) With the aid of equations, compare the reactions of phosphine and ammonia with aqueous solutions of copper and silver salts.

(b) Which of these two hydrides is the better complexing agent? Explain your answer.

(Answers on page 100)

In the last exercise you saw that phosphine behaves as a reducing agent in a situation where ammonia does not. Now you further compare the reducing powers of ammonia and phosphine by considering their reactions with oxygen and chlorine. Read about the reducing properties of the hydrides for the next exercise.

Exercise 48 (a) Phosphine is a stronger reducing agent than ammonia. Illustrate this fact with reference to the reaction of the two hydrides with oxygen and chlorine.

(b) Calculations of $\Delta H^{\ominus}$ (and $\Delta G^{\ominus}$) for the combustion of ammonia and phosphine give large negative values in each case, which indicates that ammonia might react more readily than it does. Suggest reasons for its lack of reactivity in this context.

(c) How does ammonia react with copper(II) oxide?

(Answers on page 100)

The flammability of phosphine in air is supposed to be responsible for the flickering lights ('Will o' the Wisp' or 'Jack o' Lanterns') observed near marshes, caves and tombs. Small traces of impure phosphine are produced by bacterial decay of organic matter, the impurities causing it to be spontaneously flammable.

To consolidate your knowledge of the chemistry of nitrogen and phosphorus, attempt the following Teacher-marked Exercise.

Teacher-marked Exercise Describe and account for the similarities and differences in the chemistry of nitrogen and phosphorus, using (a) the elements, (b) the hydrides and (c) the chlorides as examples.

We deal with the industrial production of ammonia in Level Two. Now we turn our attention to the most important elements in the next group of the Periodic Table.

GROUP VI: OXYGEN AND SULPHUR

The Group VI elements show the usual gradation from non-metallic to metallic properties with increasing atomic number. Oxygen and sulphur are non-metals, selenium and tellurium are semiconductors and polonium is metallic and radioactive.

As with Groups III and V, we consider the first two members of the group in more detail.

The nature of the elements

Oxygen and sulphur are widespread in nature, both as elements and in compounds, and they exhibit allotropy (polymorphism).

Objectives. When you have finished this section you should be able to:

(41) describe the appearance and structures of the allotropes of oxygen and sulphur;

(42) explain why oxygen is a gas while sulphur is a solid;

(43) state the reactions of oxygen and sulphur with selected metals and non-metals;

(44) list the common oxidation states of oxygen and sulphur.

To get a simple overall picture of Group VI, read the general introduction to the group in your textbook(s). Then look in more detail at the allotropes of oxygen and sulphur paying particular attention to their molecular structures. Also read about the physical and chemical properties of these elements.

In the next exercise you consider the allotropes of oxygen and sulphur, and investigate the similarities which exist between the elements.

Exercise 49 (a) Name and describe the appearance of the allotropes of sulphur and oxygen.

(b) Draw the shapes of the molecules for the allotropes named in (a). (Indicate any multiple bonds.)

(c) Write equations for the reactions of oxygen and sulphur with the following elements, and name the products.

(i) sodium, (iii) hydrogen,

(ii) iron, (iv) carbon.

(Answers on page 100)

Apart from the similarities in the reactions with the selected metals and non-metals and the existence of allotropes, oxygen and sulphur have very little else in common. The immediately striking difference is that oxygen is a colourless gas while sulphur is a yellow crystalline solid.

Fig.15. Microphotograph of sulphur crystallizing from olive oil solution.

In the last exercise you learned that oxygen tends to form double bonds with other oxygen atoms producing diatomic molecules, whereas sulphur tends to catenate and form S_8 ring molecules. In the next exercise you investigate the reason for this.

Exercise 50 Use the mean bond energies, $\overline{E}$, shown in Table 9 to answer the questions which follow.

Table 9

Bond	O=O	O—O	S=S	S—S
$\overline{E}$/kJ mol^{-1}	498	142	431	264

(a) Calculate the enthalpies of reaction for the following changes. Assume that S_2 and O_8 have the same structures as O_2 and S_8.

(i) $S_8(g) \rightarrow 4S_2(g)$

(ii) $O_8(g) \rightarrow 4O_2(g)$

(b) Why does oxygen consist of diatomic molecules whereas sulphur contains S_8 molecules?

(Answers on page 100)

In the next exercise you look at the electronic configurations of isolated atoms of oxygen and sulphur and explain how the possible oxidation states of the elements arise.

Exercise 51 (a) Complete a copy of Fig. 16 (not drawn to scale).

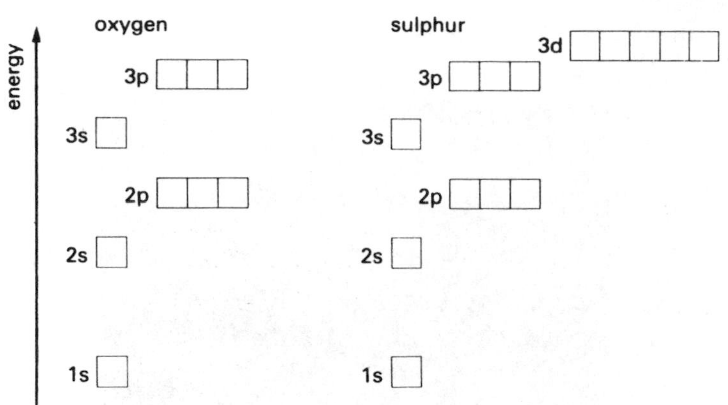

Fig.16. Electron configurations of oxygen and sulphur

(b) Why are both elements commonly divalent?

(c) What is the apparent covalency of oxygen in H_3O^+? Explain how this occurs.

(d) As well as forming the S^{2-} ion, sulphur can form 2, 4 and 6 covalent bonds with other atoms (e.g. in H_2S, SCl_2, SO_2 and SF_6). Explain how this occurs.

(e) Why is oxygen unable to form 4 and 6 covalent bonds with other atoms?

(f) The +6 oxidation state is very common for S, Se and Te but the +4 oxidation state is the most important for Po. What name do we give this effect and where have you met it before?

(Answers on page 101)

We now go on to consider some important compounds of oxygen and sulphur. Since oxygen is usually limited to the -2 oxidation state, there are many compounds of sulphur which have no oxygen analogues, e.g. SCl_4 and SF_6 exist but OCl_4 and OF_6 are not known.

The first class of compound we consider is the hydrides.

Hydrides of oxygen and sulphur

The hydrides H_2O, H_2S, H_2Se and H_2Te are all known and, with the notable exception of water, are all poisonous and pungent gases. Another anomalous property of oxygen is that it also forms another type of hydride, H_2O_2.

Objectives. When you have finished this section you should be able to:

(46) describe and, as far as possible, explain the differences between water and hydrogen sulphide in respect of -

(a) boiling-points, (c) thermal stability, (e) acidity.

(b) shapes of molecules, (d) reducing action,

Read about the properties of water and hydrogen sulphide so that you can attempt the following exercises. You have, of course, already done some work on them in other ILPAC Units.

Exercise 52 The boiling-points of water, H_2O, and hydrogen sulphide, H_2S, are 373 K and 212 K respectively. The relative molecular masses of water and hydrogen sulphide are 18 and 34 respectively.

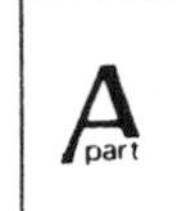

(a) By referring to the relative molecular masses, state which of the two substances you would expect to have the higher boiling-point and give a reason.

(b) Explain the differences in boiling-points in terms of inter-molecular bonding.

(Answers on page 101)

Exercise 53 Explain why the structure of hydrogen sulphide is not linear.

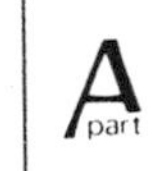

(Answer on page 101)

You are probably already aware of the high thermal stability of water. Even at 2000 °C it is only slightly decomposed into its elements. Hydrogen sulphide, however, is decomposed by strong heating. The next exercise concerns the thermal stabilities of H_2O and H_2S and the ease with which these compounds are formed from their elements.

Exercise 54 (a) Look up values of $\Delta H_f^\ominus$ and $\Delta G_f^\ominus$ for $H_2O(g)$ and $H_2S(g)$ in your data book. Comment on the ease with which these compounds can be made from their elements.

(b) Write down the mean bond energies for O—H and S—H using your data book.

(c) Account for the higher thermal stability of water compared to hydrogen sulphide.

(d) The relative instability of hydrogen sulphide is also shown by the fact that it burns readily in air. Write an equation for this reaction.

(Answers on page 101)

Since H_2S gives up its hydrogen atoms easily it is an effective reducing agent, reacting with many oxidizing agents, as you see in the next exercise.

Exercise 55 Using the information displayed in Table 10, answer the questions which follow.

Table 10

Half-reaction	$E^{\ominus}$/V
1. $S(s) + 2H^+(aq) + 2e^- \rightleftharpoons H_2S(aq)$	+0.14
2. $O_2(g) + 4H^+(aq) + 4e^- \rightleftharpoons 2H_2O(l)$	+1.23
3. $Fe^{3+}(aq) + e^- \rightleftharpoons Fe^{2+}(aq)$	+0.77
4. $MnO_4^-(aq) + 8H^+(aq) + 5e^- \rightleftharpoons Mn^{2+}(aq) + 4H_2O(l)$	+1.51
5. $SO_2(aq) + 4H^+(aq) + 4e^- \rightleftharpoons S(s) + 2H_2O(l)$	+0.45
6. $SO_4^{2-}(aq) + 4H^+(aq) + 2e^- \rightleftharpoons SO_2(aq) + 2H_2O$	+0.17
7. $\frac{1}{2}Cl_2(aq) + e^- \rightleftharpoons Cl^-(aq)$	+1.36

(a) What do the $E^{\ominus}$ values suggest about the relative strengths of water and hydrogen sulphide as reducing agents?

(b) Would you expect hydrogen sulphide to reduce the following substances:

(i) aqueous iron(III) chloride,

(ii) aqueous potassium manganate(VII),

(iii) sulphur dioxide,

(iv) sulphuric acid,

(v) chlorine?

Explain your answers.

(c) Write balanced equations for the reactions occurring in (b).

(Answers on page 102)

One property common to all Group VI hydrides is their ability to function as weak acids. The next three exercises deal with this property.

Exercise 56 Ionization of hydrogen sulphide in water occurs in two stages:

$H_2O(l) + H_2S(aq) \rightleftharpoons H_3O^+(aq) + HS^-(aq)$
hydrosulphide ion

$H_2O(l) + HS^-(aq) \rightleftharpoons H_3O^+(aq) + S^{2-}(aq)$
sulphide ion

The acid dissociation constants are, respectively, 10^{-7} mol dm^{-3} and 10^{-14} mol dm^{-3}.

(a) Identify the acid and base in each ionization stage.

(b) Arrange the substances appearing in the equations in order of decreasing concentration for a saturated solution of hydrogen sulphide.

(Answers on page 102)

In the above exercise you saw how hydrogen sulphide reacts with a weak base, water. In the next exercise you consider reactions with stronger bases.

Exercise 57 (a) What compounds will be formed if hydrogen sulphide reacts with sodium hydroxide solution so that:

(i) hydrogen sulphide is in excess,

(ii) sodium hydroxide is in excess?

(b) Write equations for the reactions occurring in (a).

(c) Why do you think most *s*-block sulphides give an alkaline aqueous solution which smells unpleasant? Illustrate your answer with reference to sodium sulphide, Na_2S.

(Answers on page 102)

In the next exercise you compare the acid strengths of the Group VI hydrides.

Exercise 58 Values of pK_a for the first ionization of the hydrides of Group VI are given below.

Hydride:	H_2O	H_2S	H_2Se	H_2Te
pK_a:	14	7	4	3

(a) How does acid strength change as the group is descended?

(b) Suggest a possible reason for this trend.

(Answers on page 102)

Other hydrides can also be formed by elements in this group, the most important being hydrogen peroxide, H_2O_2. You learned about the preparation of hydrogen peroxide in Unit I1 (The *s*-Block Elements); now you consider some of its properties.

Objectives. When you have finished this section you should be able to:

(47) describe the physical properties of hydrogen peroxide and explain its chemical instability;

(48) quote some examples of redox reactions involving hydrogen peroxide.

Read about the properties of hydrogen peroxide in your textbook(s) so that you can do the following exercises.

Exercise 59 (a) Draw the shape of the H_2O_2 molecule.

(b) Hydrogen peroxide, in its liquid state or in very concentrated solutions, is dangerously explosive but its enthalpy of formation is -187 kJ mol^{-1} ($\Delta G_f^{\ominus}$ = 118 kJ mol^{-1}). Explain this apparent anomaly.

(c) Pure hydrogen peroxide is a pale blue syrupy liquid boiling at 152 °C. How do you account for its viscous nature and high boiling-point?

(d) Would you expect hydrogen peroxide to be acidic?

(Answers on page 103)

Exercise 60 Use the standard electrode potentials given in Table 11 to answer the questions which follow:

Table 11

Half-reaction	$E^{\ominus}/V$
1. $S(s) + 2H^+(aq) + 2e^- \rightleftharpoons H_2S(aq)$	+0.14
2. $I_2(aq) + 2e^- \rightleftharpoons 2I^-(aq)$	+0.54
3. $O_2(g) + 2H^+(aq) + 2e^- \rightleftharpoons H_2O_2(aq)$	+0.68
4. $MnO_4^-(aq) + 8H^+(aq) + 5e^- \rightleftharpoons Mn^{2+}(aq) + 4H_2O(l)$	+1.51
5. $H_2O_2(aq) + 2H^+(aq) + 2e^- \rightleftharpoons 2H_2O(l)$	+1.77

(a) Write equations for the reactions in solution between hydrogen peroxide and:

(i) hydrogen sulphide,

(ii) iodide ions,

(iii) potassium manganate(VII).

(b) Write an equation for the disproportionation of hydrogen peroxide, showing the oxidation state of oxygen in reactant and products.

(c) What do you think would happen if manganese(II) ions were added to aqueous hydrogen peroxide?

(Answers on page 103)

In the Teacher-marked Exercise which now follows, you can consolidate your knowledge of Group VI elements, drawing not only on this Unit but also on information gained from other Units.

Teacher-marked Exercise

(a) Compare the properties of water and hydrogen sulphide, giving explanations of any similarities or differences that you quote.

(b) Comment on the following observations.

(i) Oxygen normally exists in the form of diatomic molecules, whereas sulphur normally exists in the form of S_8 molecules.

(ii) Oxygen does not form a hexafluoride analogous to SF_6.

(iii) There are no compounds containing the O^- or S^- ions although the electron affinities of oxygen and sulphur are -142 kJ mol^{-1} and -200 kJ mol^{-1} respectively.

(iv) Oxygen has a higher electronegativity than sulphur although more energy is released when a sulphur atom accepts an electron than when an oxygen atom accepts an electron.

In the remaining sections of Level One, we deal with the oxides and oxo-acids of sulphur. There are, of course, no corresponding compounds of oxygen.

The oxides of sulphur

Sulphur forms only two well-known oxides, sulphur dioxide, SO_2, and sulphur trioxide, SO_3, both of which are acidic.

Objectives. When you have finished this section you should be able to:

(48) describe the structure of molecules of sulphur dioxide and sulphur trioxide;

(49) describe reactions in which sulphur dioxide acts as a reducing agent.

Read about the structure, bonding and properties of sulphur dioxide and sulphur trioxide in your textbook(s) to help you with the following exercises. Look for the structure of the SO_3 molecule rather than the polymeric solid forms.

Exercise 61 (a) Draw dot-and-cross diagrams for SO_2 and SO_3.

(b) How do you explain the fact that all the S—O bond lengths in both SO_2 and SO_3 are identical?

(c) Describe the shapes of the SO_2 and SO_3 molecules, indicating the bond angles approximately.

(Answers on page 103)

Exercise 62 Use the information in Table 12 to answer the questions which follow.

Table 12

Half-reaction	$E^{\ominus}/V$
1. $Cr_2O_7^{2-}(aq) + 14H^+(aq) + 6e^- \rightleftharpoons 2Cr^{3+}(aq) + 7H_2O(l)$	+1.33
2. $Fe^{3+}(aq) + e^- \rightleftharpoons Fe^{2+}(aq)$	+0.77
3. $MnO_4^-(aq) + 8H^+(aq) + 5e^- \rightleftharpoons Mn^{2+}(aq) + 4H_2O(l)$	+1.51
4. $SO_2(aq) + 4H^+(aq) + 4e^- \rightleftharpoons S(s) + 2H_2O(l)$	+0.45
5. $SO_4^{2-}(aq) + 4H^+(aq) + 2e^- \rightleftharpoons SO_2(aq) + 2H_2O$	+0.17
6. $Cl_2(aq) + 2e^- \rightleftharpoons 2Cl^-(aq)$	+1.36

(a) Would you expect sulphur dioxide to reduce the following reagents?

(i) $MnO_4^-(aq)$, (iii) $Cl_2(aq)$,

(ii) $Fe^{3+}(aq)$, (iv) $Cr_2O_7^{2-}(aq)$.

(b) Write balanced equations for the reactions which do occur.

(c) Which of the reactions forms the basis of a useful test for gaseous sulphur dioxide?

(Answers on page 104)

You know already that the oxides of sulphur are the anhydrides of sulphurous and sulphuric acids. In the next section, you learn more about these oxoacids and some others which you may not have met before.

The oxoacids and oxosalts of sulphur

Sulphur forms many oxoacids, like nitrogen, phosphorus and chlorine, its near neighbours in the Periodic Table. The commonest acid is sulphuric acid, H_2SO_4. The other acids are better known as their salts.

Objectives. When you have finished this section you should be able to:

(50) explain why sulphuric acid is a stronger acid than sulphurous acid;

(51) state and explain the physical and chemical properties of sulphuric acid;

(52) state and explain the chemical properties of the following anions -

(a) sulphite, SO_3^{2-}, (c) thiosulphate, $S_2O_3^{2-}$,

(b) sulphate, SO_4^{2-}, (d) peroxodisulphate, $S_2O_8^{2-}$ (persulphate);

(53) describe the structure and bonding of the sulphite, sulphate and thiosulphate ions.

An aqueous solution, often called 'sulphurous acid', H_2SO_3, is made by passing sulphur dioxide into water. It is slowly oxidized by air to sulphuric acid. The solution contains the ions SO_3^{2-}, HSO_3^- and H_3O^+ as well as dissolved SO_2 molecules, but there is no strong evidence for the molecule H_2SO_3. Therefore, sulphurous acid is best represented by the equilibrium shown in the next exercise.

Exercise 63 Solutions of sulphur dioxide are believed to contain hydrated molecules of $SO_2(aq)$ which ionize as follows.

$SO_2(aq) + H_2O(l) \rightleftharpoons H^+(aq) + HSO_3^-(aq)$ ......(1)

$HSO_3^-(aq) \rightleftharpoons H^+(aq) + SO_3^{2-}(aq)$ ....(2)

(a) From your data book write down the K_a and pK_a values for the two ionizations shown above.

(b) Name the ions shown in equations (1) and (2).

(c) Write equations for the two ionization stages which occur in dilute sulphuric acid.

(d) From your data book write down the K_a and pK_a values for the two ionization stages in sulphuric acid.

(e) Compare the acid strengths of sulphuric and 'sulphurous' acids.

(Answers on page 104)

Sulphuric acid is a reagent which you have used both in its dilute and concentrated forms throughout this course. In the Teacher-marked Exercise which follows, you are asked to bring together the information you have gained from various ILPAC Units about sulphuric acid.

Teacher-marked Exercise

Sulphuric acid is one of the most versatile reagents used in the laboratory. Discuss this statement by referring to reactions which illustrate its behaviour

(a) as an acid,

(b) in the displacement of other acids from their salts,

(c) as a sulphonating agent,

(d) as an oxidizing agent,

(e) as a dehydrating agent.

We deal with the industrial production and uses of sulphuric acid in Level Two. Now you investigate, by experiment, the properties of some of the oxo-salts of sulphur.

EXPERIMENT 3

Investigating some reactions of the oxo-salts of sulphur

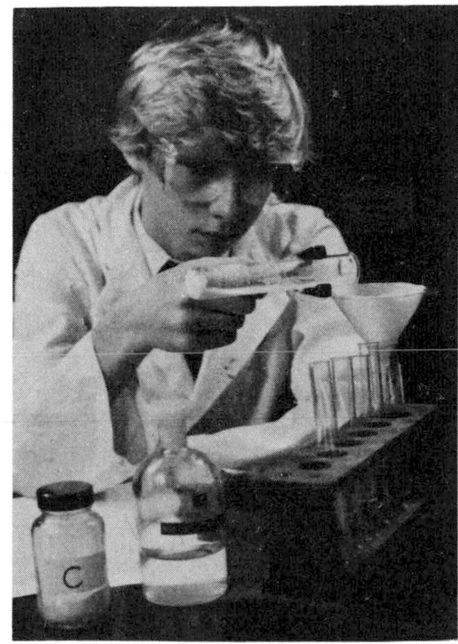

Aim

The purpose of this experiment is to illustrate the redox reactions of some oxo-anions of sulphur, some of which can be used as tests for these ions.

Introduction

You are asked to carry out some simple test-tube reactions on solutions and solid samples of the following salts:

sodium sulphite, Na_2SO_3,

sodium sulphate, Na_2SO_4,

sodium thiosulphate, $Na_2S_2O_3$,

sodium peroxodisulphate, $Na_2S_2O_8$ (sodium persulphate).

In some cases you may not be able to interpret the reactions fully, but be sure to record your observations clearly and precisely.

Requirements

safety spectacles
protective gloves
10 test-tubes in rack
sodium sulphite solution, 0.2 M Na_2SO_3
sodium sulphate solution, 0.2 M Na_2SO_4
sodium thiosulphate solution, 0.2 M $Na_2S_2O_3$
sodium peroxodisulphate solution, 0.2 M $Na_2S_2O_8$
(persulphate)
hydrochloric acid, dilute, 2 M HCl
Bunsen burner and bench protection mat
wood splints
potassium dichromate(VI) solution, acidified, 0.1 M $K_2Cr_2O_7$
strips of filter paper
silver nitrate solution, 0.1 M $AgNO_3$
'silver residues' bottle
iodine solution, 0.2 M I_2 in KI(aq)
potassium iodide solution, 0.5 M KI
iron(III) chloride solution, 0.5 M $FeCl_3$
sodium hydroxide solution, 2 M NaOH
test-tube holder
spatula
sodium sulphite-7-water, $Na_2SO_3 \cdot 7H_2O$
sodium sulphate-10-water, $Na_2SO_4 \cdot 10H_2O$
sodium thiosulphate-5-water, $Na_2S_2O_3 \cdot 5H_2O$
sodium peroxodisulphate, $Na_2S_2O_8$
boiling-tube
sulphur, powdered, S
filter funnel
filter papers

Hazard warning

Several of the solutions listed are corrosive. A toxic gas is released in small quantities in test 1. Therefore YOU MUST:

WEAR SAFETY SPECTACLES AND GLOVES
WORK AT A FUME CUPBOARD (FOR TEST 1)
SMELL GASES CAUTIOUSLY

Procedure

Perform tests 1 to 5 on separate portions (about 1 cm^3) of solutions of the four oxo-salts provided.

1. Working at a fume cupboard, add an equal volume of dilute hydrochloric acid, a few drops at a time. Warm gently (do not boil) and test any gas which you can see or smell. Record your observations in a larger copy of Results Table 4 and infer what you can from them.

2. Add about 2 cm^3 of silver nitrate solution, a few drops at a time. Pour residues into the bottle provided.

3. Add a few drops of iodine solution.

4. Add a few drops of potassium iodide solution.

5. Add two drops of iron(III) chloride solution, followed by a few drops of dilute hydrochloric acid. Warm gently (do not boil) for half a minute and then add sodium hydroxide solution.

6. Heat small separate portions (about 0.5 g) of the solid oxo-salts in a series of clean test-tubes. Test any gases evolved. Record your observations and inferences in your copy of Results Table 5.

7. Place about 0.5 g of finely-powdered sulphur in a boiling-tube and add about 10 cm^3 of sodium sulphite solution. Boil the mixture for 2-3 minutes and then filter.

8. Perform tests 1 to 5 on portions of the filtrate from step 7. Record your observations in the last column of Results Table 5 and attempt to identify the new species, X, in the filtrate.

Results Table 5

	Observations and inferences				
Test	Na_2SO_3	Na_2SO_4	$Na_2S_2O_3$	$Na_2S_2O_8$	'X'
1. Dilute hydrochloric acid. Warm.	(a)	(b)	(c)	(d)	
2. Silver nitrate solution.	(e)	(f)	(g)	(h)	
3. Iodine solution in aqueous potassium iodide.	(i)	(j)	(k)	(l)	
4. Potassium iodide solution.	(m)	(n)	(o)	(p)	
5. Iron(III) chloride solution. Acidify, warm, add alkali.	(q)	(r)	(s)	(t)	
6. Effect of heat on solid.	(u)	(v)	(w)	(x)	

(Specimen results on page 105)

Questions

1. With the aid of your textbook(s) interpret your observations as far as you can, writing equations where possible, especially for (a), (c), (i), (k), (l) and (q). Insert oxidation numbers for sulphur in the equations.

2. Which of the reactions illustrate(s) disproportionation?

3. Which of the oxo-salts is: (i) the strongest oxidizing agent, (ii) the strongest reducing agent, and (iii) the most stable salt?

4. Apart from the reactions used in the experiment describe, from your previous knowledge, how you would distinguish between sodium sulphite and sodium sulphate.

5. What is the identity of the new species, X, produced by heating sodium sulphite solution with sulphur?

(Answers on page 105)

In the next exercise you investigate the structures of the sulphate, sulphite and thiosulphate ions.

Exercise 64 (a) Draw some 'electron-pair' structures for SO_4^{2-} to explain why the ion is symmetrical in shape.

(b) What shape would you expect for the SO_3^{2-} ion?

(c) What new bonds appear in the formation of thiosulphate ions by heating aqueous sulphite ions with sulphur?

(Answers on page **104**)

Now you can apply your knowledge of the chemistry of sulphur to selenium.

Exercise 65 To answer this question, use the information provided below on selenium and its compounds.

Selenium occurs below sulphur in Group VI of the Periodic Table. It has an atomic number of 34 and a relative atomic mass of 79. The successive molar ionization energies, in 10^3 kJ mol^{-1}, are

0.94, 2.1, 3.1, 4.1, 7.1, 7.9, 15

Crystals of selenium dioxide contain chains of selenium and oxygen atoms:

```
—Se —a— O —a— Se —a— O —a— Se —a— O —a— Se
 |b           |b            |b            |b
 O            O             O             O
```

The bond lengths are a = 0.178 nm, b = 0.173 nm.

Selenium forms compounds analogous to sulphites and sulphates.

$H_2SeO_3(aq) + 4H^+(aq) + 4e^- \rightleftharpoons Se(s) + 3H_2O(l)$; $E^\ominus$ = +0.74 V

$SeO_4^{2-}(aq) + 4H^+(aq) + 2e^- \rightleftharpoons H_2SeO_3(aq) + H_2O(l)$; $E^\ominus$ = +1.15 V

(a) Explain the pattern in the first seven ionization energies of selenium.

(b) (i) Draw a diagram to show the electronic structure ('dot-and-cross') of selenium dioxide. Only the outer electronic shells of one unit of the chain need be shown.

(ii) What reason can you suggest for the bond lengths being different?

(Continued on page 53.)

Exercise 65 (continued)

(c) Insert in (a copy of) the chart of redox potentials the information relating to the reduction of H_2SeO_3 to Se, and the reduction of SeO_4^{2-} to H_2SeO_3.

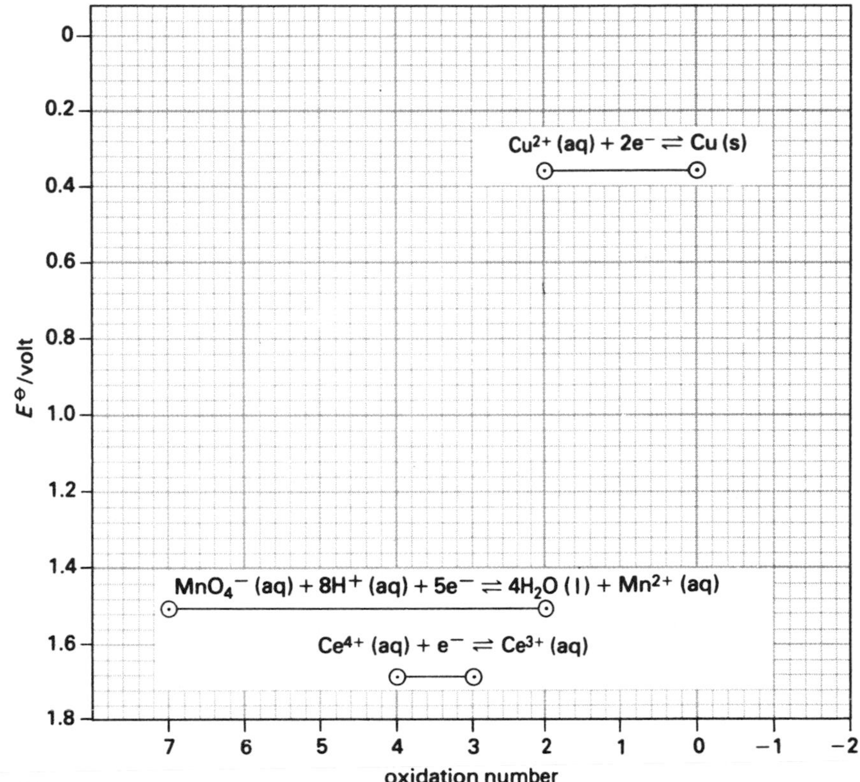

Fig.17.

(d) Using the information displayed on the chart, answer the following questions:

(i) What would you expect to observe if acidified $KMnO_4$ were added to H_2SeO_3 solution?

(ii) Write a balanced equation for the reaction between Ce^{4+} and H_2SeO_3 solutions.

(e) (i) Give the conventional cell diagram of a cell suitable for measurement of the standard e.m.f. of the reaction between Cu(s) and SeO_4^{2-}(aq).

(ii) Deduce the standard e.m.f. of such a cell.

(Answers on page 106)

Your teacher may suggest that you do the End-of-Unit Practical Test (page 82) before you start on Level Two. The test is based on the work you have done in Level One, and is intended primarily for students who will take a practical examination.

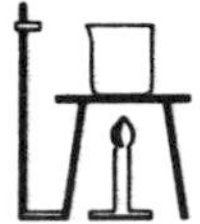

LEVEL ONE CHECKLIST

You have now reached the end of Level One of this Unit. The following is a summary of the objectives in Level One. Read carefully through it and check that you have adequate notes on the sections you have studied.

If you have studied all the sections on Group III, you should now be able to:

(1) compare physical properties of boron and aluminium such as appearance, electrical conductivity and ionic radius;

(2) list the likely oxidation states of the elements in Group III;

(3) state how aluminium reacts with acids and alkalis;

(4) describe how aluminium sulphate can be prepared from aluminium;

(5) describe the bonding and structure of the fluorides and chlorides of boron and aluminium;

(6) describe the hydrolysis of the chlorides of boron and aluminium;

(7) explain the acidic nature of solutions of boric(III) acid, $B(OH)_3$, and aluminium salts;

(8) write a chemical equation for the reaction between boron oxide and water;

(9) list some commercial uses of aluminium oxide;

(10) compare the stabilities of boron oxide and aluminium oxide;

(11) & (15) describe the effect of heat on aluminium sulphate, and list some of its uses;

(13) state the general formula of alums;

(12) & (14) describe the preparation of potassium aluminium sulphate (potash alum) and its reactions with solutions of sodium hydroxide, barium chloride and sodium carbonate;

If you have studied all the sections on Group V, you should now be able to:

(16) describe the structures of the red and white allotropes of phosphorus;

(17) explain why nitrogen is a fairly unreactive gas while phosphorus is a reactive solid;

(18) describe any reactions of nitrogen and phosphorus with (a) hydrogen, (b) oxygen, (c) chlorine, (d) selected metals, (e) alkalis and (f) concentrated nitric acid;

(19) explain why nitrogen forms only one chloride whereas phosphorus forms two;

(20) describe and explain the hydrolysis of NCl_3 and PCl_3;

(21) describe the hydrolysis of PCl_5 and the chlorides of the other elements in Group V;

(22) place the common oxides of (a) nitrogen and (b) phosphorus in order of increasing stability;

(23) outline the preparation of the oxides NO, NO_2, N_2O_4, P_4O_6 and P_4O_{10};

(24) explain the meaning of the term odd-electron molecule and draw dot-and cross diagrams for NO, NO_2 and N_2O_4;

(25) draw the structures of P_4O_6 and P_4O_{10};

(26) compare the reactions of the oxides N_2O, NO and NO_2 with (a) chlorine, (b) metals, (c) iron(II) ions and (d) water;

(27) state and explain the effect of dinitrogen oxide, N_2O, on a glowing splint;

(28) describe the hydrolysis of the oxides of phosphorus;

(29) & (30) illustrate the redox reactions of nitric acid, nitrous acid and nitrites;

(31) explain the unstable nature of nitrous acid;

(32) draw the shapes of the species H_3PO_4, PO_4^{3-}, HPO_4^{2-} and $H_2PO_4^-$;

(33) state some uses of phosphoric (V) acid and phosphates;

(34) & (37) list the hydrides formed by Group V elements and explain the trend in the thermal stability of the tri-hydrides as the group is descended;

(35), (36), (38) & (40) compare ammonia and phosphine with reference to molecular shape, boiling-point, solubility in water, base strength, reducing ability and complexing ability;

(39) describe the effect of heat and of water on phosphonium iodide;

If you have studied all the sections on Group VI, you should now be able to:

(41) & (42) describe the appearance and structure of the allotropes of oxygen and sulphur and explain why oxygen is a gas while sulphur is a solid;

(43) describe the reactions of oxygen and sulphur with selected metals and non-metals;

(44) list the common oxidation states of oxygen and sulphur;

(45) describe and, as far as possible, explain the difference between water and hydrogen sulphide in respect of (a) boiling-point, (b) molecular shape, (c) thermal stability, (d) reducing action, and (e) acidity;

(46) & (47) account for the physical properties and chemical instability of hydrogen peroxide and describe some of its redox reactions;

(48) describe the structures of the molecules of sulphur dioxide and trioxide;

(49) describe reactions in which sulphur dioxide acts as a reducing agent;

(50) & (51) describe the physical and chemical properties of sulphuric acid and explain why it is a stronger acid than sulphurous acid;

(52) & (53) describe the shapes and chemical properties of the oxo-anions of sulphur, SO_3^{2-}, SO_4^{2-}, $S_2O_3^{2-}$, $S_2O_8^{2-}$.

LEVEL ONE TEST

Since your syllabus may not require you to study everything in Level One, we have decided to give you a selection of questions for each of the three Groups III, V and VI. Your teacher will tell you which questions to attempt, and the duration of the test.

You will not be required to attempt all the questions if you have studied all three groups.

LEVEL ONE TEST

Section A - Group III

1. (a) Suggest why aluminium(III) fluoride is ionic but the corresponding chloride is covalent. (3)

   (b) Discuss the molar reacting quantities in the following description and outline the reaction scheme by constructing representative equations:

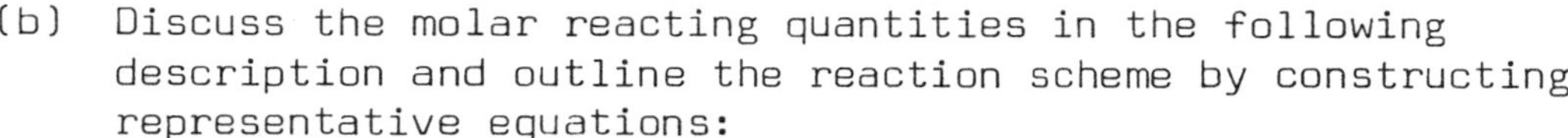

   0.1 mol of aluminium reacts with 0.1 mol of aqueous potassium hydroxide to form solution X. If solution X is treated with 0.2 mol of sulphuric acid, a crystalline salt containing both potassium and aluminium ions can be crystallized from solution. (6)

   (c) Write the equation for the hydrolysis of aluminium(III) chloride. (4)

2. (a) How and under what conditions does aluminium react with (i) chlorine, (ii) hydrochloric acid, (iii) aqueous potassium hydroxide? (9)

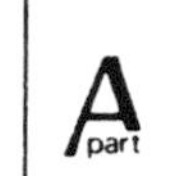

   (b) Explain why an aqueous solution of aluminium sulphate has a pH less than 7. (3)

   (c) The relative molecular mass of anhydrous aluminium chloride in benzene solution is 267, but measurement of the density of the vapour is consistent with a relative molecular mass of 133.5. How do you explain these results? (4)

   (d) Give, with explanation, two chemical properties of compounds of boron that illustrate the non-metallic nature of the element. (4)

Section B - Group V

3. (a) Give the atomic number of nitrogen, and the electronic configuration of its isolated atom. (1)

A

   (b) For nitrogen molecules, N_2, nitrate ions, NO_3^-, and ammonium ions, NH_4^+, respectively:

      (i) state the oxidation number of nitrogen,

      (ii) show the structural formula, including the outer electrons,

      (iii) describe in words, or by a diagram, the shape. (9)

   (c) Describe briefly, giving reagents, reaction conditions, and equations, how compounds containing nitrogen of oxidation number +2, +3 and +4, respectively, could be conveniently prepared from nitric acid or a nitrate. (6)

(d) In the reaction: $N_2H_6O + IO_3^- + 2H^+ + Cl^- \rightarrow N_2 + ICl + 4H_2O$

only the oxidation numbers of the nitrogen and the iodine alter. Calculate from the equation the oxidation number of the nitrogen in N_2H_6O. (2)

4. (a) 'Ammonia can act as a base and as a complex forming agent'. Discuss this statement with the aid of suitable examples, giving what explanation you can in terms of the electronic structure of the ammonia molecule. (5) A part

(b) How and under what conditions does nitric oxide (NO) react with

(i) iron(II) sulphate, (iii) potassium hydroxide,

(ii) copper, (iv) chlorine? (8)

5. When white phosphorus is heated carefully with sodium hydroxide solution, a colourless, poisonous, inflammable gas is evolved. This gas contains 91.02% P and 8.98% H. (H = 1; P = 31.) A part

(a) Write the formula for the white phosphorus molecule. (1)

(b) Draw a diagram to illustrate the geometry of the white phosphorus molecule. (2)

(c) Deduce the empirical formula of the gas evolved in the statement above. (3)

(d) This gas is very weakly basic, and reacts with hydrogen iodide to form a solid compound. Write the equation for this reaction. (2)

(e) By analogy with ammonium iodide (or otherwise), write the equation for the reaction between the solid formed in (d) and sodium hydroxide solution. (2)

(f) The gas formed from the original white phosphorus is spontaneously inflammable in air. Write the equation for this combustion, naming the products. (4)

(g) Explain why NCl_3 is the highest chloride of nitrogen but phosphorus can form PCl_5. (2)

(h) 1.07 g of a nitrogen compound was boiled with an excess of sodium hydroxide solution and all the nitrogen was released as ammonia gas. This ammonia was found to neutralize 200 cm^3 0.100 M hydrochloric acid. Calculate the percentage by mass of nitrogen in the compound. (N = 14) (5)

6. (a) Write the electronic configurations of nitrogen and phosphorus in the ground state in terms of *s* and *p* electrons. (2) A

(b) For the three hydrides NH_3, PH_3 and AsH_3,

(i) Give the shapes of the molecules and state how the bond angle varies from $NH_3 \rightarrow PH_3 \rightarrow AsH_3$. (3)

(ii) State which is the strongest and which is the weakest Brønsted-Lowry base and write an equation to show the strongest behaving as a base. (4)

(iii) Give an explanation, in terms of bonding, of the difference in the boiling-points of ammonia and phosphine, which are 240 K and 186 K respectively. (4)

7. (a) Attempt physico-chemical explanations of:

   (i) the relative pK_b values (alkalinities) of ammonia and phosphine (PH_3), (4)

   (ii) the different types of hydrolysis undergone by NCl_3 and PCl_3. (6)

   (b) Contrast, with examples where appropriate, the oxidizing powers of nitric acid, HNO_3, and phosphoric acid, H_3PO_4. (5)

   (c) Draw bond diagrams to represent the structures of NO and P_4O_{10} commenting on any significant features. (5)

8. Identify the substance X below; explain fully the changes recorded and give equations wherever possible.

   X is a white solid which sublimes on heating. When heated with sodium hydroxide a pungent gas is evolved which reduces heated copper(II) oxide to copper. X can be prepared by mixing equal volumes of two colourless gases. X evolves a violet vapour, sulphur dioxide and some hydrogen sulphide when heated with concentrated sulphuric acid. (6)

Section C - Group VI

9. (a) Give the atomic number of sulphur and the electronic configuration of its isolated atom. (1)

   (b) For sulphur dioxide (SO_2) and hydrogen sulphide (H_2S) molecules and sulphate ions (SO_4^{2-}), respectively:

   (i) state the oxidation number of the sulphur,

   (ii) show the structural formula, including the outer electrons,

   (iii) describe in words, or by a diagram, the shape. (9)

   (c) Describe briefly, giving reagents, reaction conditions, and equations, how substances containing sulphur of oxidation number (i) +4, (ii) +6, and (iii) 0, respectively, could be obtained from sulphur dioxide. (9)

   (d) In the reaction: $Na_2H_{10}S_2O_8 + 4Br_2 \rightarrow 2H_2SO_4 + 2NaBr + 6HBr$

   only the oxidation numbers of the sulphur and bromine alter. Calculate from the equation the oxidation number of the sulphur in $Na_2H_{10}S_2O_8$. (2)

10. (a) Briefly explain what is meant by the term allotropy in relation to sulphur. (4)

   Draw a diagram to illustrate the molecular structure of a solid allotrope of sulphur. (2)

   (b) When radioactive sulphur (^{35}S) slowly dissolves in hot aqueous sodium sulphite to give a solution of compound A, and the resulting solution is acidified, a precipitate B is formed which is the only radioactive product, no radioactivity remaining in solution. Explain these observations and indicate what information may be deduced regarding the structure of A. (6)

11. Group VI of the Periodic Table contains the elements oxygen, sulphur, selenium, tellurium, and polonium in increasing order of atomic number. The most common oxidation numbers in this group of elements are -2, +4 and +6.

A

(a) Write the formula of a hydride of sulphur in the -2 oxidation state. (1)

(b) Write the formula of an oxide of selenium in the +4 oxidation state. (1)

(c) Write the formula of an oxoacid of tellurium in the +6 oxidation state. (1)

(d) Which of these elements is likely to be radioactive? (1)

(e) Write an equation representing the thermal decomposition of the compound in (a). (2)

(f) Put the hydrides of this Group in order of increasing stability to heat. (2)

(g) Using iron sulphide and dilute sulphuric acid as reagents, and a tap funnel, conical flask, delivery tube and Bunsen burner as apparatus, draw a diagram to show how you would demonstrate the thermal decomposition of hydrogen sulphide. (4)

Say how you would identify the products. (2)

12. (a) The equation: $H_2SeO_4(aq) + 2OH^-(aq) \rightarrow 2H_2O(l) + SeO_4^{2-}(aq)$

A part

represents the reaction of selenic(VI) acid with hydroxyl (hydroxide) ions.

(i) Which species in this equation is donating protons? (1)

(ii) Which species in this equation is accepting protons? (1)

(iii) Explain why this reaction is regarded as a neutralization. (2)

(b) Suggest a theoretical interpretation for the lesser volatility of water when compared with hydrogen sulphide. (2)

(c) Indicate how sodium trioxothiosulphate (thiosulphate) is used in photography and in volumetric analysis. (3)

(d) Explain why the structure of hydrogen sulphide is not linear. (4)

LEVEL TWO

Some industrial chemistry

In this part of the Unit we deal with some important industrial processes which involve *p*-block elements and their compounds.

For Group III we consider the extraction of aluminium from its ore; for Group V, the industrial manufacture of ammonia and nitric acid; and for Group VI, the manufacture of sulphuric acid.

We begin with the extraction of aluminium.

The extraction of aluminium from its ore

The importance of aluminium in our society has increased dramatically in the last hundred years. It has a unique combination of properties which make it useful in such diverse applications as overhead power-cables, saucepans, aircraft bodies and milk-bottle tops. These and many other uses have made aluminium the next most important industrial metal after iron.

The rise in importance has been made possible by the relatively cheap production of the metal from its ore.

Objectives. When you have finished this section you should be able to:

(54) state how pure aluminium oxide is obtained from bauxite;

(55) explain how the metal is extracted from its oxide by electrolysis;

(56) explain why this method of extraction is chosen;

(57) explain how and why the metal is anodized;

(58) list the uses of aluminium and relate these to its properties.

The following article by R. Lancashire appeared in 'Education in Chemistry', May 1982. It discusses the production of pure aluminium oxide from bauxite and the subsequent electrolysis of aluminium oxide to produce aluminium.

Read the passage carefully and then answer the exercises which follow. You are not expected to remember all the details of the process. The exercises are designed to focus your attention on the more important aspects.

R Lancashire

Bauxite and aluminium production

The term *Bauxite* is derived from Les Baux, a town near Arles in southern France where, in 1821, Berthier obtained a sample of a red clay-like sediment, rich in aluminium. It appears that bauxite was originally considered to be a new mineral, however, later work revealed considerable variations in mineralogical composition, physical appearance and mode of occurrence. The name *Bauxite ore* is generally applied to all bauxites which contain not less than 45–50 per cent of one or more of the hydrated aluminium oxides, and not more than 20 per cent Fe_2O_3 and 3–5 per cent combined silica, and which are considered economically mineable, now or in the foreseeable future. Table 1[2] shows some of the main minerals present in bauxite deposits.

The first commercial alumina (Al_2O_3) extraction from bauxite was attributed to Henri Sainte-Claire Deville[3] about 1854, whereupon the price of aluminium quickly tumbled to a thirtieth of its price. This method soon gave way to that of Karl Joseph Bayer[4] in 1888, and the Bayer Process caused a further marked reduction in price of aluminium metal which eventually led to it becoming an everyday commodity rather than a precious metal.

The Bayer Process, which continues to be the most economical method of manufacturing alumina, is schematically summarised in *Fig. 1* and involves the following operations:

1 dissolution of the alumina at elevated temperatures;
2 addition of flocculants then separation and washing of the insoluble impurities of bauxite (red mud) to recover the soluble aluminate and caustic soda;
3 precipitation of pure Gibbsite by seeding the cooled, clarified solution with previously precipitated crystals;
4 regeneration of the solutions for recycling to step *1* by evaporation of the water introduced by the washings;
5 heating the precipitated Gibbsite, to 1100 °C (calcination) to remove the chemically combined water, hence producing alumina.

Fig. 1. The Bayer process (numbers refer to description in text).

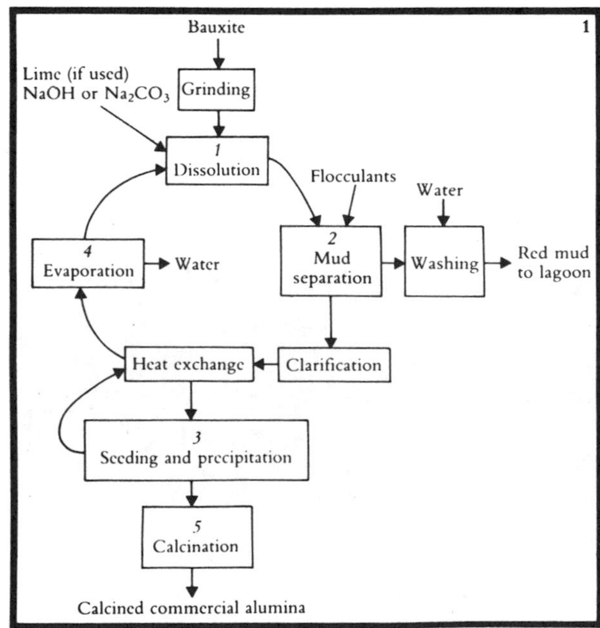

In order to remove the iron oxides and most of the silicon oxides present, the ore is first treated with aqueous sodium hydroxide. The digestion process takes advantage of the solubility of amphoteric aluminium oxides to form a solution of aluminate ions, whilst the basic iron oxide, which does not dissolve, is separated by filtration. Thus

$$\text{Gibbsite}\quad Al_2O_3.3H_2O + 2NaOH \xrightarrow{135\text{–}145\,°C} 2NaAlO_2 + 4H_2O \quad (\gamma\ Al(OH)_3)$$

$$\text{Boehmite}\quad Al_2O_3.H_2O + 2NaOH \xrightarrow{205\text{–}245\,°C} 2NaAlO_2 + 2H_2O \quad (\gamma\ AlO\ OH)$$

$$\text{Diaspore}\quad Al_2O_3.H_2O + 2NaOH \xrightarrow[\text{High pressure}]{\text{High temp}} 2NaAlO_2 + 2H_2O \quad (\alpha\ AlO\ OH)$$

Complete extraction from diasporic bauxite requires stronger caustic solutions, in addition to higher temperatures and pressures. In general, the reaction equilibria above move to the right with increases in caustic soda concentration and temperature. The actual conditions employed at each process plant are determined by the types of bauxite most commonly encountered there. In practice this means that for deposits containing the more easily recoverable Gibbsite only, production costs are much lower than when Boehmite or Diaspore are present.

The control of silica in the conventional Bayer process is most important and, in fact, ores having reactive silica greater than 7 per cent cannot be economically processed.

Unlike quartz, which is considered virtually non-reactive at Gibbsite extraction temperatures, some minerals, including kaolins, dissolve rapidly and the reaction of the silica can give rise to appreciable loss of caustic soda and aluminium.

The control of silica[5] is generally carried out during, or prior to, the digestion step, and generally involves dissolution, *eg* for kaolin

$$Al_2O_3.2SiO_2 + NaOH \longrightarrow Na_2SiO_3$$

and desilication via precipitation,

$$Na_2SiO_3 + NaAlO_2 \longrightarrow Na_2O.Al_2O_3.2SiO_2$$

Dissolution is necessary to supersaturate the liquid to a point where the sodalite formed acts as a seed to precipitate more sodalite. The rate of precipitation is found to increase with temperature, however at 135–150 °C it is significantly slower than is required for complete Gibbsite extraction which occurs within minutes. The need for desilication

Table I. Main Minerals of Bauxite Deposits.[2]

Name	Composition
Gibbsite (Hydrargillite)	$\gamma - Al(OH)_3$, $\alpha - Al_2O_3.3H_2O$
Boehmite	$\gamma - AlOOH$, $\alpha - Al_2O_3.H_2O$
Diaspore	$\alpha - AlOOH$, $\beta - Al_2O_3.H_2O$
Hematite	$\alpha - Fe_2O_3$
Goethite	$\alpha - FeOOH$
Magnetite	Fe_3O_4
Siderite	$FeCO_3$
Ilmenite	$FeTiO_3$
Anatase	TiO_2
Rutile	TiO_2
Brookite	TiO_2
Halloysite	$Al_2O_3.\ 2\ SiO_2.3H_2O$
Kaolinite	$Al_2O_3.2SiO_2.2H_2O$
Quartz	SiO_2

therefore means that material must be held at the digestion temperature long enough to allow the silica to precipitate.

The insoluble residues remaining after digestion (red mud) contain iron oxides, sodium aluminium silicate, titanium oxide and various other metal oxides. Disposal of the washed muds is a major problem and these are generally lagooned. It has been estimated[6] that approximately 1 km^2 of lagoon area is required for a plant processing 3.3m t of bauxite per year; however, the same lagoon may be used for several years. Much research has been directed toward extraction of various elements from the red mud, but no economic process has yet been developed. There have also been attempts to convert the mud into building products and cements. However, a report[7] recently prepared for the US Environmental Protection Agency concerning the use of red muds, concluded that there was no possibility for utilising the muds that could significantly reduce the need for impoundment in the near future.

Production of aluminium

In 1886, Hall and Héroult[8], working independently, simultaneously discovered that electrolysis of molten cryolite (Na_3AlF_6) in which alumina was dissolved, led to the formation of metallic aluminium. The Hall–Héroult process[6] is still the basis for which nearly all aluminium is produced. In the modern process, a little fluorspar (CaF_2), aluminium fluoride (AlF_3) and lithium fluoride (LiF) are added with the alumina to reduce the melting point of the cryolite and improve the efficiency. Carbon anodes and cathode are used; the aluminium metal is deposited onto the cathode which is also the melt container, while oxygen is evolved at, and consumes, the anode forming CO_2 which escapes as gas. (*Fig. 2*).

It is believed that during electrolysis, cryolite ionises to form AlF_6^{3-} which dissociates to AlF_4^- and F^- thus:

$$Na_3AlF_6 \longrightarrow 3Na^+ + AlF_6^{3-}$$
$$AlF_6^{3-} \rightleftharpoons AlF_4^- + 2F^-$$

Alumina then dissolves at low concentrations according to the following reactions:

$$Al_2O_3 + 4AlF_6^{3-} \longrightarrow 3Al_2OF_6^{2-} + 6F^-$$
$$Al_2O_3 + AlF_6^{3-} \longrightarrow 3AlOF_2^-$$

At the cathode where aluminium is deposited, hexafluoroaluminate ions are discharged

$$4AlF_6^{3-} + 12e^- \longrightarrow 4Al + 24F^-$$

whereas at the anode, the oxyfluoride ions discharge forming CO_2 and reforming AlF_6^{3-} ions, thus

$$6AlOF_2^- + 3C + 24F^- \longrightarrow 3CO_2 + 6AlF_6^{3-} + 12e$$

The overall cell reaction can therefore be written as:

$$2Al_2O_3 + 3C \longrightarrow 4Al + 3CO_2$$

An interesting feature of the electrolysis is given by the thermodynamic data[9]. The energy changes occuring are:

$$Al_2O_3 \xrightarrow{\text{electrolysis}} 2Al + \tfrac{3}{2}O_2 \qquad \Delta G_{1260K} = 1255\ kJ$$
$$\tfrac{3}{2}O_2 + \tfrac{3}{2}C \longrightarrow \tfrac{3}{2}CO_2 \qquad \Delta G_{1260} = -603\ kJ$$

consequently, for the overall process

$$Al_2O_3 + \tfrac{3}{2}C \longrightarrow 2Al + \tfrac{3}{2}CO_2 \qquad \Delta G_{1260} = 652\ kJ$$

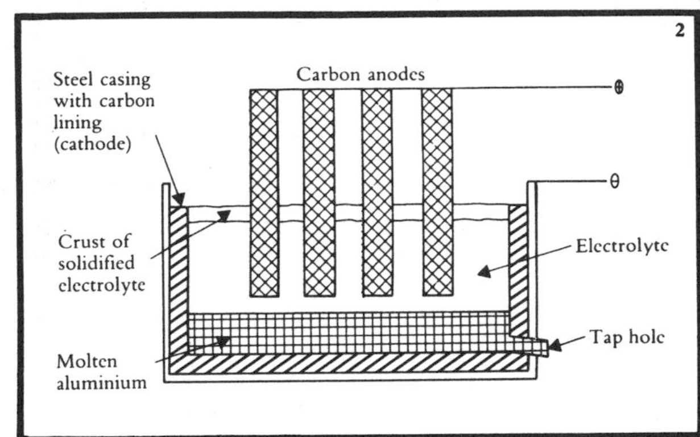

Fig. 2. The Hall–Héroult electrolytic cell.

That is, the consumption of the carbon anodes during the electrolytic extraction, reduces the total energy input required by nearly a half.

Whilst aluminium is second only to iron as the most abundant of the metals used by man, it is relatively difficult to separate from its parent rock. The rapid growth of the aluminium industry in the 20th century has been founded on

Table 2. Aluminous minerals constituting potential sources of alumina.[13b]

Mineral	Formula	Wt per cent Al_2O_3	Occurrence
Mullite	$Al_6Si_2O_{13}$	72	Rare naturally, but common in fly ash
Andalusite Sillimanite Kyanite	Al_2SiO_5	63	Metamorphic minerals
Staurolite	$Fe_2Al_9O_6(Sio_4)_4(O,OH)_2$	Up to 54	Metamorphic mineral
Kaolinite	$Al_2O_3.2SiO_2.2H_2O$	39.5	Alteration of feldspar
Muscovite	$K.Al_2(AlSi_3O_{10})(OH)_2$	Up to 38	Metamorphic, igneous or pegmatitic mineral
Alunite	$K.Al_3(SO_4)_2(OH)_6$	37	Alteration product of near-surface volcanic rocks
Plagioclase	$(Na,Ca)(Al,Si)AlSi_2O_8$	20 to 36	Common constituent of igneous rocks
Dawsonite	$NaAl(OH)_2CO_3$	35	Rare diagenetic mineral
Nepheline	$(K, Na)AlSiO_4$	32	Common constituent of alkaline igneous rocks
Pyrophyllite	$Al_4(Si_8O_{20})(OH)_4$	28	Alteration of feldspar
Leucite	$K(AlSi_2O_6)$	23	Rare igneous mineral
Montmorillonite	$Al_4(Si_4O_{10})_2(OH)_4$	c20	Alteration of feldspar
Illite	$K.Al_4(Si_{8-y}Al_y)O_{20}(OH)_4.nH_2O$	c20	Alteration of feldspar
Crandallite	$CaAl_3(PO_4)_2(OH)_5.H_2.O$	19.6	Leached phosphoric sand

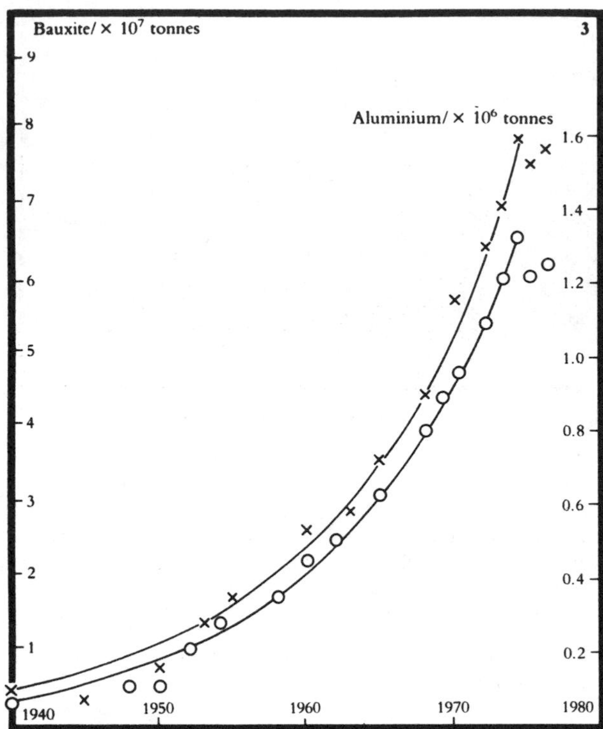

Fig. 3. World bauxite and aluminium production: ×, bauxite; ○, aluminium.

a number of rich bauxite deposits. In brief, bauxite is the product of *in situ* weathering during which components such as soda, potash, lime, magnesia and some silica were removed in solution from the parent rock. This process required a warm humid climate of continuous moisture so that rich deposits are largely found in tropical or sub-tropical regions.

Figure 3[10] shows the dramatic increase in bauxite and aluminium production over the past 40 years. The discontinuity of these graphs at 1974–1975 coincides with the creation of the International Bauxite Association(IBA). The majority of the world's bauxite now comes from the member countries of IBA, who in 1974 introduced significant increases in tariffs and taxation. It has been claimed[11] that these price increases led to some countries, particularly those with large aluminium industries and small bauxite deposits, accelerating their prospecting and research activities to consider itilising indigenous aluminium-bearing minerals for aluminium production. However, the US for example, still imports over 90 per cent of its bauxite. The situation with bauxite is not unique, since the US also imports 90 per cent or more of manganese, cobalt and chromium needs.[12]

Alternatives to bauxite and the Bayer process

Non-bauxite sources of aluminium are not a new option. There are a large number and vast quantities of aluminium-bearing minerals and rocks. However, while most of these comprise silicates, which are resistant to chemical dissolution and extremely difficult to process, some are considered to constitute potential sources of alumina (see Table 2).[13b]

The early work on non-bauxite sources was prompted by the potential disruption of bauxite supplies during World War II. At that time Germany for example, used domestic clay and andalusite as a minor source of aluminium.

After World War II, the aluminium industry relied almost entirely on bauxite as a raw material, and there was neither reason nor incentive to pursue alternatives.

The presently known world bauxite reserves and resources and their geographical distribution are given in Table 3,[13] together with the 1979 production estimates for the western world.[14] The reserves exist in sufficient quantities to satisfy normal requirements for 50–100 years. In addition, because of the need to avoid medium-term shortages, it is believed that both the US and USSR have stockpiled sufficient bauxite to meet their needs for at least 12 months.

Despite this, however, it is considered that these reserves and resources are less secure and economically attractive than

Table 3. World bauxite reserves: resources[13a] and estimated western world production figures for 1979[14] (figures in million tonnes).

Countries		Reserves	Resources	Production
North America				
United States		40	400	1.7
Caribbean & Central America				
Costa Rica		120	100	–
Dominican Republic		40	20	0.5
Haiti		10	60	0.6
Jamaica		1,600	800	0
	Subtotal	1,770	980	12.0
South America				
Brazil		4,070	30,000	1.4
Colombia		–	70	–
French Guiana		–	1,700	–
Guyana		1,810	25,000	3.0
Suriname		500	10,000	5.0
Venezuela		500	1,500	–
	Subtotal	6,880	68,270	
Africa				
Cameroon		1,500	10,000	–
Ghana		250	300	0.3
Guinea		11,500	10,000	12.0
Sierra Leone		400	300	0.7
	Subtotal	13,650	20,600	
Asia				
India		1,100	1,000	2.1
Indonesia		700	2,000	1.0
Malaysia		50	15	0.3
Turkey		50	200	0.2
	Subtotal	1,900	3,215	
Europe				
France		30	200	2.0
Greece		450	300	2.7
Hungry		200	200	–
USSR		300	300	–
Yugoslavia		200	500	2.9
	Subtotal	1,180	1,500	
Oceania				
Australia		5,000	6,000	26.1
Solomon Islands		60	100	–
	Subtotal	5,060	6,100	
Others		300	7,000	
Total		30,780	108,065	74.5

Reserves = Measured, indicated and inferred reserves.
Resources = Identified sub-economic and undiscovered resources.
Production figures for western world only.

they once were. Coupled to this are increased costs and drawbacks related to the Bayer process such as the need to process ores of a particular quality (high extractable alumina (40–60 per cent), low reactive silica (< 7 per cent)), and the problems of red mud disposal. These factors have led to renewed interest in non-bauxite sources of aluminium.

The only peace-time aluminium industry based partly on the use of non-bauxite materials is in the USSR, where alunite and nepheline concentrate are used as the raw materials. Nepheline concentrate cannot be directly compared with other non-bauxite sources since it is not a crude ore but a by-product in the production of apatite for fertilizer.

The experimental processes currently in operation either at industrial scale or pilot-plant include:[11,15,16]

1. Pechiney-Ugine-Kuhlmann (H-plus process) (French)
2. Cirzymek (Polish)
3. Nitric Acid – ion exchange (American)
4. Hydrochloric acid – isopropyl ether extraction (American)
5. Lime – soda sinter (American)
6. Nepheline concentrate (Soviet Union)

Of these, the Pechiney H-plus process[11a, 17] is the nearest competitor to the Bayer process in terms of running costs and energy requirements. This process, which can utilise a variety of raw materials ranging from clay and kaolin to tailings from coal mines with alumina contents as low as 20 per cent; involves the following steps:

a crushing of the raw material
b digestion in 60–70 per cent H_2SO_4 at 130–140 °C
c filtration and recrystallisation of aluminium sulphate
d introduction to the solution of anhydrous HCl
e cooling and crystallisation of aluminium chloride
f filtration and calcination to form alumina.

The extraction efficiency of these alternative processes are usually lower than for the Bayer process and in general much more energy is required to extract the same quantity of alumina.

A Cryolite crystal.

In conclusion, the following factors should ensure that bauxite retains its position as the primary aluminium ore for the foreseeable future:

- the existence of adequate reserves
- the present state and potential for future development of the Bayer–Hall–Héroult technologies
- extraction of by-products, for example, vanadium and gallium. Gallium[18] is recovered from the aluminate liquor in countries including US, France, Germany and Hungary, and Bayer liquor extractions represent the major source of the world's supplies of this increasingly useful element.

The US aluminium industry is committed to the use of bauxite as its source of primary aluminium for the following reasons:

- it is based on Bayer processed bauxite and changes to another process and material would involve major changes in technology;
- it has major overseas investments in the mining and processing sectors and in shipping installations;
- the present industry–government joint ownership of mines and other installations in some countries is based on long-term agreements;
- it is only with high government subsidy that the aluminium industry would be able to use non-bauxite aluminous raw materials.

Consequently it is unlikely that within the next 20–30 years that aluminium companies will need to heed the words of Sir Fred Hoyle[19] and 'simply turn to clay'.

Dr Robert Lancashire is a lecturer in inorganic chemistry at the University of the West Indies, Jamaica.

References

1 P. Berthier, *Ann. Mines*, 1821, **6,** 531.
2 I. Valeton, *Development of Soil Science 1 Bauxites*. Elsevier Publishing, 1972.
3 H. Sainte-Claire Deville, *Ann. Chim. Pys.*, 1854, **43,** 27. *Compt. Rend.*, 1854, **46,** 452.
4 K. J. Bayer, *Chem. Zeitung*, 1888, **12,** 1210.
5 R. A. Meikle, *Journal of the Geological Society of Jamaica Proceedings of Bauxite Symposium, No II,* 3 Oct, 1973, p 30.
6 *Kirk-Othmer Encyclopedia of Chemical Technology*, 3rd edn, Vol 2. Wiley-Interscience, 1978.
7 B. K. Parekh and W. M. Goldberger, *U.S. Environmental Protection Agency Technology Series, EPA-600/2-76-301,* Dec 1976.
8a *The Aluminium Industry in Brief.* Alcan Jamaica, 1969.
8b O. A. Battista, *Chemistry*, 1969, **42,** 14.
9 J. W. Moore and E. A. Moore, *Environmental chemistry*, 275–276. Academic Press, 1976.
10 *Year-Book of American Bureau of Metal Statistics*, 1976.
11a N. A. Shaikh, *2nd 'Industrial Minerals' international conference report from Munich*, 1976.
11b S. H. Patterson, *American Scientist*, May-June (1977).
12. U.S. Bureau of Mines, *AIME Conference*, Feb 1980.
13a V. G. Hill in *Journal of the Geological Society of Jamaica*, Special issue, Proceedings of Bauxite Symposium IV, pp 3–19 June, 1980.
13b N. W. Bliss in *Journal of the Geological Society of Jamaica*, Special Issue, Proceedings of Bauxite Symposium IV, pp 201–226, June 1980.
14 *Mining Annual Review*, 1980.
15a P. W. Johnson, F. A. Peters and R. C. Kirby, *U.S. Bureau of Mines Report of Investigation 6431*, 1964.
15b F. A. Peters and P. W. Johnson, *US Bureau of Mines Information Circular 8648*, 1974.
16 G. Parkinson, *Chemical Engineer (UK)* 1971, **78,** 83.
17a *Chemical Week*, 1974, March, **40.**
17b J. A. Osborne, *Proceedings of the Royal Aust. Chem. Inst.*, 1977, **44,** 31.
18 *Chemicals and technology: an encyclopedic treatment, Vol 3, Metals and ores.* Barnes and Noble, 1970.
19 F. Hoyle, *Energy or extinction —the case for nuclear energy*. London: Heinemann, 1977.

Exercise 66 (a) Explain the meaning of the following terms used in the article:

(i) dissolution,

(ii) flocculants,

(iii) calcination.

(b) In the Bayer process, bauxite is separated into commercial alumina and 'red mud'.

(i) What are the main constituents of red mud?

(ii) What gives red mud its colour?

(iii) Why is sodium hydroxide (or other alkali) used in the extraction of alumina from bauxite?

(iv) How is silica removed from bauxite?

(c) (i) State the name and formula of the molten substance in which alumina is dissolved before electrolysis.

(ii) Name three other substances which are added to the melt. Why are they added?

(iii) Write equations for the cathode and anode reactions and the overall cell reaction.

(iv) Explain why very little cryolite is used up.

(d) (i) Why are the anodes made of carbon?

(ii) Why do the anodes need renewal?

(iii) The carbon anodes are usually renewed continuously by allowing the heat of the melt to bake a graphite paste injected into moulds from the top. Why is this preferred to the simple replacement of solid anodes?

(e) Complete a copy of the flow diagram in Fig. 18 which summarises the essential steps in the extraction of aluminium from bauxite.

(Answers on page 107)

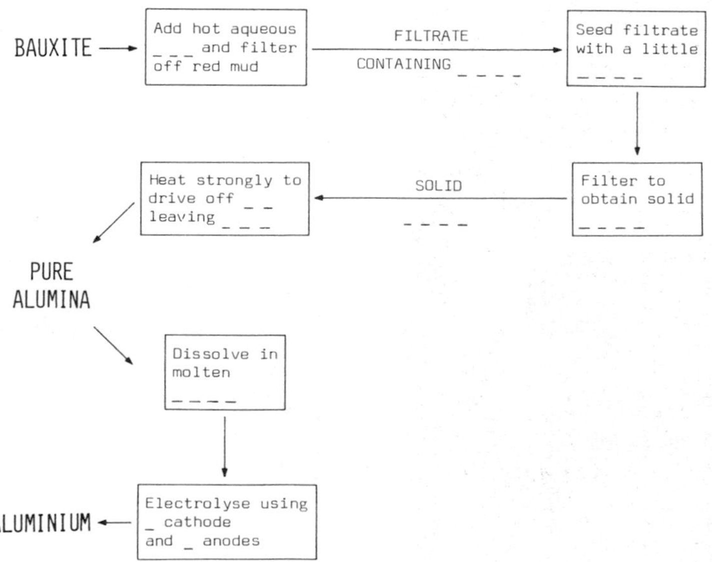

Fig.18. Summary of aluminium production

You have probably gathered from the article that the reactions occurring during electrolysis are complex and not fully understood. If you cannot remember them you should, at the very least, know that the reactions stated in many textbooks are over-simplified:

Cathode reaction: $Al^{3+} + 3e^- \rightarrow Al$

Anode reaction: $O^{2-} \rightarrow \frac{1}{2}O_2 + 2e^-$

The next exercise is concerned mainly with the economic and social aspects of aluminium production.

Exercise 67

(a) Why is the disposal of red mud a major problem?

(b) What uses have been suggested for red mud?

(c) Why do you think world bauxite and aluminium production has increased dramatically over the past 40 years?

(d) Suggest reasons why the U.S.A. and the U.S.S.R. may have stockpiled sufficient bauxite to meet their requirements for at least twelve months.

(e) Which non-bauxite materials have been used in the U.S.S.R. to make aluminium?

(f) What factors have led to a renewed interest in non-bauxite sources of aluminium?

(g) Why do you think it is unlikely that non-bauxite materials will overtake bauxite as the main aluminium raw materials in the next 20 years?

(Answers on page 107)

Fig.19. Electrolytic cells for aluminium production

You learned in Level One that the reactivity of aluminium is masked by a thin coherent layer of aluminium oxide. Without this protective layer, aluminium would not be such a useful metal. The range of uses can be extended still further by making the oxide layer much thicker in a process called anodizing. Anodized aluminium is not only more resistant to corrosion, but it can be made more attractive by surface dyeing.

In the next experiment you can anodize and dye a piece of aluminium. If you do not do this experiment we suggest that you read the procedure so that you know, in outline, how the process is carried out.

EXPERIMENT 4

Anodizing aluminium

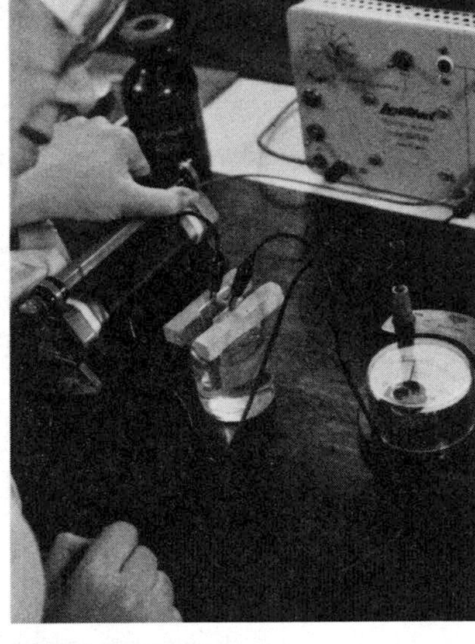

Aim

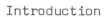

The purpose of this experiment is to demonstrate the effect of anodizing aluminium on its electrical conductivity and behaviour towards dyes.

Introduction

Aluminium is anodized by making it the anode during the electrolysis of a solution which normally releases oxygen - you will use dilute sulphuric acid. Instead of oxygen, aluminium ions are released and these are immediately hydrolysed to give a layer of hydrated oxide. After electrolysis you compare anodized and unanodized aluminium by testing their conductivities and immersing them in a dye solution.

Requirements

safety spectacles
two pieces of sheet aluminium, 7 cm x 3 cm, mounted on wooden bars
2 beakers, 100 cm^3
forceps or tweezers
cotton-wool
1,1,1-trichloroethane, CH_3CCl_3
sulphuric acid, dilute, 1 M H_2SO_4
Bunsen burner, tripod, gauze and bench mat
thermometer, 0-100 °C
DC supply, 12 V
ammeter, 1 A
rheostat, 10 Ω, 4 A
4 connecting leads, two with crocodile clips at one end
2 large pins
dye solution, e.g. alizarin red

Procedure

A. Anodizing

1. Mark one of the wooden supports for the electrodes with a 'plus' sign. This carries the piece of aluminium to be used as the anode.

2. Working at a fume cupboard, remove any grease from the surface of the anode by swabbing with cotton-wool soaked in 1,1,1-trichloroethane and held in forceps or tweezers. From now on, hold the anode only by its wooden support.

3. Pour about 75 cm^3 of dilute sulphuric acid into a small beaker, heat to about 40 °C and stand it on the bench.

4. Place the electrodes in the beaker and set up the circuit shown in Fig. 20. Make sure the clean anode is connected to the positive terminal of the supply.

5. Switch on the DC supply and adjust the rheostat to give a current of 0.3 A. Maintain this current for at least 15 minutes (longer if it is convenient), adjusting the rheostat if necessary to keep the current constant.

6. Switch off the supply. Disconnect the electrodes, remove them from the beaker and wash them with distilled water. Has their appearance changed?

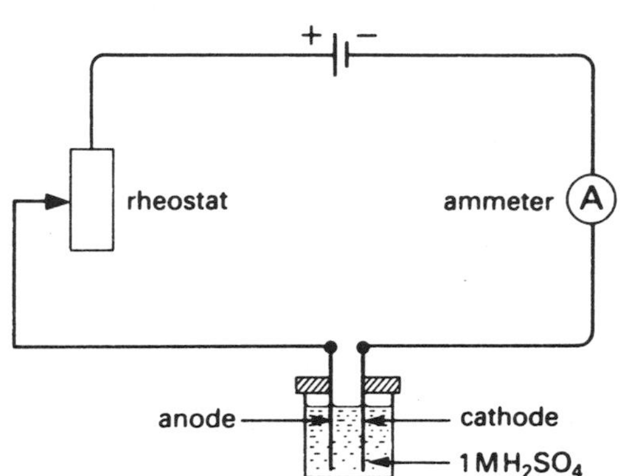

Fig.20.

B. Conductivity testing

7. Clip a large pin to each of the leads you had previously connected to the electrodes. Adjust the rheostat so that when the two pins touch each other, the current is no greater than 1 A.

8. Touch each pin lightly on the surface of the cathode and note the ammeter reading. Repeat for the anode. Is there any difference? Now press the pins more firmly on to the anode surface. If this does not change the ammeter reading, try scratching the surface with the pins.

C. Dyeing

10. Place spots of dye solution on both anode and cathode and leave for 2-3 minutes. (If you have enough dye, you can immerse the electrodes.) Rinse the electrodes with water and inspect them.

Questions

1. How does anodizing affect aluminium with regard to its

   (a) appearance, (b) conductivity, (c) susceptibility to dyes?

2. You probably noticed that you had to reduce the variable resistance during the electrolysis in order to prevent the current from falling. Suggest two reasons for this.

3. In what applications might anodizing be

   (a) an advantage, (b) a disadvantage?

(Answers on page 108)

To consolidate your knowledge of aluminium production and its uses we suggest you attempt one or both of the following Teacher-marked Exercises. You will need to read a little more about the uses of aluminium, looking particularly for the relationships between uses and properties.

Teacher-marked Exercise

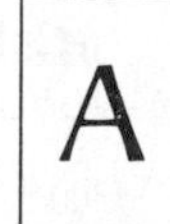

Aluminium, the most abundant metal in Earth's crust, exists in nature in the form of its hydrated oxide called bauxite, and in a large number of common materials and clays in the form of complex silicates of aluminium and other metals.

Aluminium was first isolated in 1872 by warming the anhydrous chloride with potassium. Later the potassium was replaced by sodium and, until 1886, this was the only method available for producing aluminium; consequently, aluminium was little more than a chemical curiosity. The cheap production of aluminium was made possible by C.M. Hall's discovery, in 1886, that a solution of alumina in molten cryolite can be electrolysed, and that aluminium collects at the cathode. The price of aluminium in the middle of the last century was £17.00 an ounce; its price in 1979, although its production is heavily dependent on electricity, was about 40 pence a pound.

The development of the production of aluminium as the second most important industrial metal can be summarised as follows:

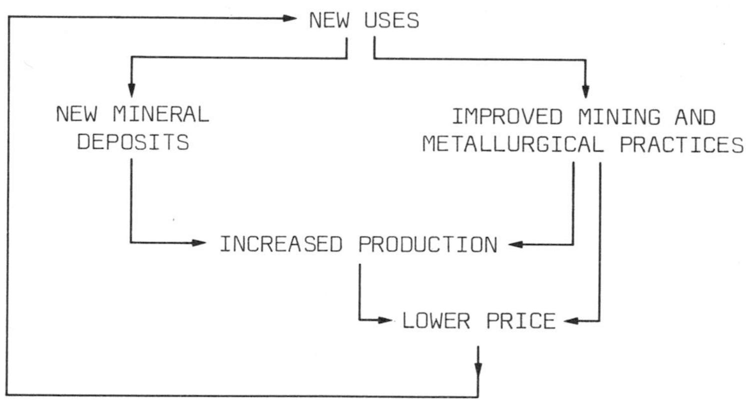

Fig.21.

(a) Give a brief account of the modern production of aluminium including in your account the design of the electrolytic cell, the electrolyte, the conditions and the reactions which occur at the electrodes.

(b) (i) Use the above diagram to explain how aluminium has become a most important industrial metal.

(ii) Give reasons to explain why the electrolysis of anhydrous aluminium chloride is not possible.

(iii) Explain, with examples, how aluminium's increasing industrial use is determined by its physical and chemical properties.

(c) State and explain two major problems which will have to be investigated if aluminium is to remain cheaply available in the twenty-first century.

Teacher-marked Exercise (a) How would you anodize a piece of aluminium? Discuss the principles underlying this form of corrosion protection of the metal.

(b) Give an account of the uses of aluminium, emphasizing its advantages and disadvantages in each case.

The next exercise illustrates another aspect of the extraction of aluminium. If your syllabus includes the interpretation of Ellingham diagrams, you will have studied them in Unit I5 (Transition Metals) in connection with the extraction of iron. Revise this work, if necessary, or omit the exercise if it does not relate to your syllabus.

Exercise 68 Study the Ellingham diagrams in Fig. 22 and answer the questions which follow.

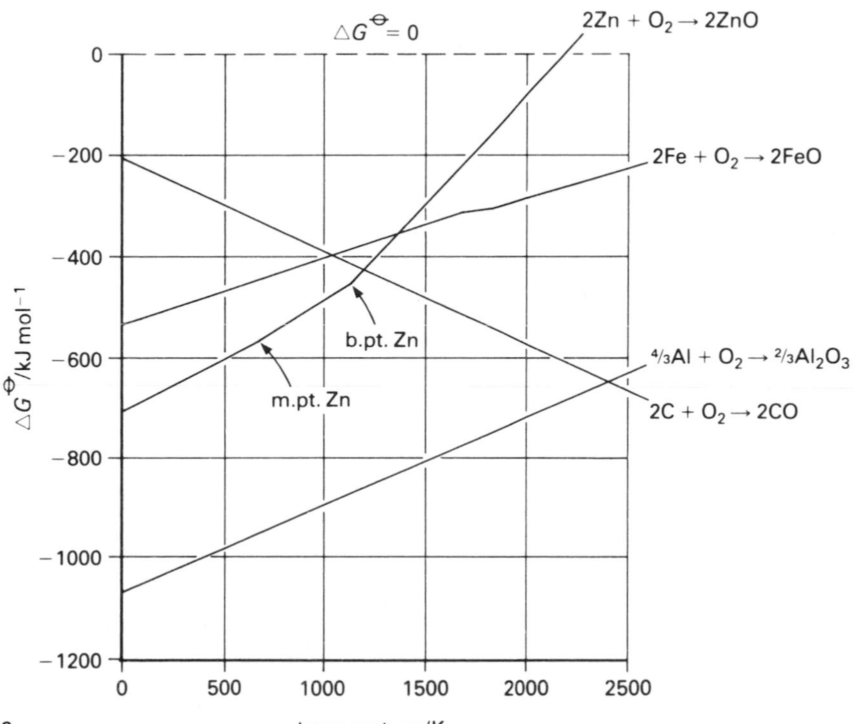

Fig.22.

(a) State the temperatures above which carbon will reduce the following oxides:

(i) ZnO,

(ii) FeO,

(iii) Al_2O_3.

(b) Explain why aluminium and iron are extracted by different methods.

(Answers on page 108)

You have now completed the sections on the industrial chemistry of the Group III element, aluminium. In the following sections we turn to Group V and consider first the industrial production of ammonia.

The industrial production of ammonia

You probably know something about this topic from your earlier studies, in which case some of the work you do now will be revision.

Objectives. When you have finished this section you should be able to:

(59) describe the Haber process for the production of ammonia from nitrogen and hydrogen;

(60) state the sources from which nitrogen and hydrogen are obtained;

(61) explain the choice of temperature and pressure in the process;

(62) state the effect of the catalyst on the equilibrium position and on the rate at which equilibrium is reached;

(63) list some of the important uses of ammonia.

Read about the Haber process for the manufacture of ammonia, paying particular attention to the choice of temperature and pressure. You may need to refer to your notes on Unit P2 (Equilibrium I: Principles) to remind yourself about Le Chatelier's principle before attempting the next two exercises.

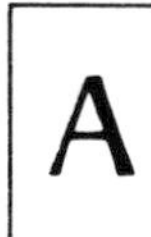

Exercise 69 is based on the following extract from an article in an education journal. Read the passage carefully.

Extract from "The Fixation of Nitrogen"

(S.P.S. Andrew, Education in Chemistry, July 1978)

The fixation of atmospheric nitrogen in the form of ammonia is one of the foundations of the modern chemical industry. Combined in the form of ammonium nitrate, urea or ammonium phosphate, over 50 million tonnes per year are used worldwide as fertilisers. Other uses of fixed nitrogen amount to some 10 million tonnes per year, explosives, dyestuffs and polymer manufacture predominating.

Ammonia production. In the U.K. ammonia currently is entirely made using natural gas (methane) to produce hydrogen. The simplified overall stoichiometry of ammonia production is:

$$(\tfrac{1}{2}N_2 + \tfrac{1}{8}O_2) + \tfrac{5}{8}H_2O + \tfrac{7}{16}CH_4 \rightarrow NH_3 + \tfrac{7}{16}CO_2; \quad \Delta H^{\ominus} = -6.7\ \text{kJ mol}^{-1}$$

The use of methane to make hydrogen for ammonia production was the result of the development of the methane-steam reforming process. This process essentially makes a hydrogen-containing gas by reacting methane with steam over a nickel-on-*refractory* catalyst. The methane required by this stoichiometry is sufficient in theory to supply the energy for the complete chemical transformation to produce gaseous ammonia. In practice extra fuel, amounting to about a further 50 per cent over the stoichiometric, must be used for raising the temperature of the gases leaving the steam reformer to about 1100 °C, a temperature at which the equilibrium of the reaction:

$$CH_4 + H_2O \rightleftharpoons CO + 3H_2 \text{ (the methane-steam reaction)}$$

is displaced well to the right.

Synthesising ammonia. Two factors are of crucial importance in synthesis - firstly, the equilibrium of the reaction, secondly, its rate. The reaction equilibrium:

$$\tfrac{1}{2}N_2(g) + \tfrac{3}{2}H_2(g) \rightleftharpoons NH_3(g); \quad \Delta H^{\ominus} = -47.3 \text{ kJ mol}^{-1}$$

is markedly temperature and pressure sensitive (Fig. 23). The rate of the reaction is determined by the efficacy of the synthesis catalyst.

Since the early days of commercial ammonia synthesis this catalyst has been metallic iron promoted by potassium hydroxide (KOH) and containing a small amount of mixed refractory oxides such as alumina (Al_2O_3), silica (SiO_2) and magnesium oxide (MgO). Fabrication of the catalyst is by melting together the ingredients in their oxide forms and casting the molten iron oxide (Fe_3O_4) melt. The resulting solid sheet is then broken up to give 5-10 mm chunks. Finally, it is reduced. In its active state the catalyst consists predominantly of iron crystallites of a few hundred Ångstrom (1 Å = 0.1 nm) units in size. These crystallites are separated by amorphous refractory oxides and partially covered by alkali promoter.

In order to maintain catalyst activity it is necessary to eliminate catalyst poisons from the gas entering the ammonia synthesis reactor. Hydrogen sulphide and water vapour chemisorb on the surface of the iron rendering it ineffective as a catalyst. In addition, water results in a recrystallisation of the catalyst structure giving larger iron crystallites and hence an even lower exposed iron surface area with consequent loss in catalytic activity. Water vapour can enter the catalyst either as itself or as carbon monoxide (CO) or carbon dioxide (CO_2), for both of these gases will be hydrogenated to methane and water vapour over the catalyst. Rigorous exclusion of hydrogen sulphide (H_2S), water, carbon monoxide (CO) and carbon dioxide (CO_2) from the catalyst is, therefore, desirable.

The commercial operating range of ammonia synthesis catalyst is between 400 °C and 540 °C. Below 400 °C, the catalyst is not sufficiently active and above 540 °C it loses surface area by sintering too rapidly. In order, therefore, to obtain reasonable conversions per pass through the converter, synthesis pressures in modern plants fall in the range 8080 - 35 350 kPa (80 - 350 atm).

Contrary to what might at first be thought, this choice of synthesis pressure is little affected by considerations of the total mechanical power requirements for compressing the nitrogen and hydrogen feed as, over a wide range of pressures (10 100 - 30 300 kPa: 100 - 300 atm), the sum of the power required for compression plus power for driving a refrigeration system for condensing the product liquid ammonia plus power for returning unconverted hydrogen and nitrogen to the converter remains virtually constant. The lower gas compression power of low pressure synthesis is almost exactly balanced by the higher refrigeration power.

The use of lower synthesis pressures has been greatly influenced by the availability of suitable cheap rotary gas compressors. Steam turbine drives are usually employed for these compressors, the steam being almost wholly generated by heat rejected from the process. By thus utilising waste heat for driving the machinery of the plant, the only thermal inefficiency is the result of having to burn methane in the reformer furnace. The energy efficiency of the whole process of making ammonia is, therefore, about 65 per cent.

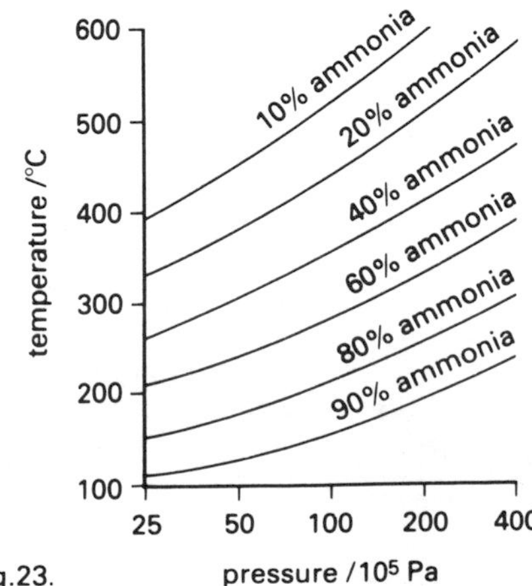

Fig.23.

Exercise 69 Answer the following questions, which relate to the preceding extract.

(a) (i) Give the names and formulae of two nitrogen-containing compounds used as fertilizers.

(ii) Give the name of a widely-used nitrogen-containing polymer.

(b) (i) Outline the steam-reforming of methane.

(ii) Explain the meaning of the word *refractory*.

(iii) Deduce the sign of the enthalpy change for the reaction:

$$CH_4(g) + H_2O(g) \rightarrow CO(g) + 3H_2(g)$$

Give your reasoning.

(iv) For the equilibrium:

$$CH_4(g) + H_2O(g) \rightleftharpoons CO(g) + 3H_2(g)$$

give an expression for the equilibrium constant, K_p, and explain what happens to the equilibrium partial pressure of the hydrogen when the total pressure of the steam is increased.

(c) (i) What two factors are of crucial importance in the synthesis of ammonia?

(ii) Describe the nature and fabrication of the catalyst used in ammonia synthesis.

(iii) What effect does water vapour have on the catalyst? How does it enter the catalyst?

(d) Using the information given in the passage, discuss how the economy of the ammonia synthesis depends upon the catalyst, power requirements, pressure and temperature.

(Answers on page 108)

The next exercise deals with the conditions of temperature and pressure employed in the Haber Process.

Fig.24. Ammonia production (ICI)

Exercise 70 In the Haber process for the manufacture of ammonia, the reactants enter the reaction vessel in the ratio one mole of nitrogen to three moles of hydrogen. The equation is

$$N_2(g) + 3H_2(g) \rightleftharpoons 2NH_3(g); \quad \Delta H^{\ominus} = -100 \text{ kJ mol}^{-1} \text{ at 200 atm and 800 K}$$

After leaving the reaction vessel, the gases pass over a heat exchanger before the ammonia is removed and unreacted gases re-cycled. Argon has to be 'blown off' from time to time.

The percentages of ammonia present in the equilibrium mixture under different conditions, are snown in the graph.

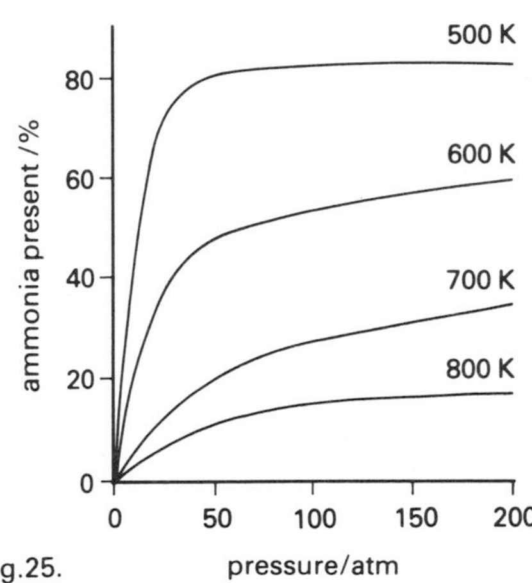

Fig.25.

In practice, the process is operated at 200 atm and 800 K.

(a) Give ONE reason for

(i) NOT using a higher temperature than 800 K,

(ii) NOT using a lower temperature than 800 K.

(b) Give ONE reason for NOT using a pressure exceeding 200 atmospheres.

(c) How could ammonia be separated from the other two gases on the output side of the plant?

(d) The heat exchange ensures that the heat of the reaction is not wasted, but does useful work elsewhere. Give one other reason why the heat exchanger is important to the efficiency of the reaction process.

(e) (i) What is the equilibrium constant expression in terms of p_{N_2}, p_{H_2}, p_{NH_3}?

(ii) How would the presence of argon affect the partial pressure of ammonia and hence the yield?

(iii) Where does the argon come from?

(f) The equilibrium partial pressure of nitrogen is 42 atm out of a total pressure of 200 atm.

(i) What is the partial pressure of hydrogen?

(ii) Calculate the partial pressure of ammonia and the percentage of ammonia in the equilibrium mixture.

(iii) Give ONE reason why the commercial process is more economical when the reaction is NOT allowed to reach equilibrium.

(Answers on page 109)

Much of the ammonia produced by the Haber Process is used to manufacture nitric acid, which is used as an oxidizing agent and nitrating agent as well as an acid. It is required for making both inorganic and organic nitrates, such as ammonium nitrate and ethyl nitrate, and organic nitro-derivatives such as trinitrotoluene (TNT) and nitroglycerine. These products include useful fertilisers and explosives.

The manufacture of nitric acid

Objectives. When you have finished this section you should be able to:

(64) describe the manufacture of nitric acid;

(65) use Le Chatelier's principle to explain the operating conditions;

(66) state the main uses of nitric acid.

In the next exercise, the process is described for you but you apply your knowledge of physical chemistry to answer the questions.

Exercise 71 Nitric acid is manufactured by the catalytic oxidation of ammonia and the subsequent reaction of the product with water. The ammonia gas is mixed with a large excess of air and passed at atmospheric pressure through a grid made up of layers of gauze of composition platinum 90%, rhodium 10%. The reaction takes place at about 900 °C. Some recent manufacturing plants, which can be rather smaller, operate this stage at a pressure of 8 atmospheres.

A

$$4NH_3(g) + 5O_2(g) \rightleftharpoons 4NO(g) + 6H_2O(g); \quad \Delta H^{\ominus}_{1200} = -903 \text{ kJ mol}^{-1}$$

The gases leaving the converter are cooled and mixed with more air to promote a second oxidation reaction.

$$2NO(g) + O_2(g) \rightleftharpoons N_2O_4(g); \quad \Delta H^{\ominus}_{400} = -116 \text{ kJ mol}^{-1}$$

$$N_2O_4(g) \rightleftharpoons 2NO_2(g); \quad \Delta G^{\ominus}_{400} = -13 \text{ kJ mol}^{-1}$$

The reaction mixture is then compressed to 8 atmospheres and passed up absorption towers 30 metres high, down which water is flowing.

$$3NO_2(g) + H_2O(l) \rightleftharpoons 2HNO_3(aq) + NO(aq); \quad \Delta H^{\ominus}_{298} = -135 \text{ kJ mol}^{-1}$$

The nitric acid flowing out of the absorption tower is coloured green due to dissolved nitrogen oxide.

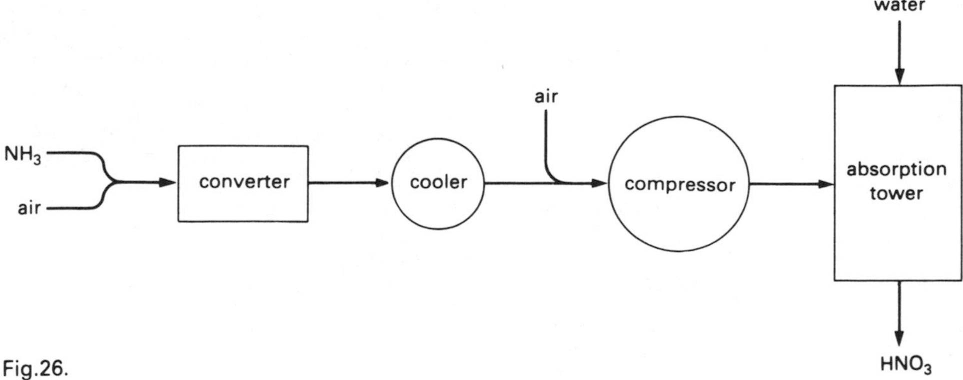

Fig.26.

Exercise 71 (cont.)

(a) Write down the equilibrium constant expression for K_p for the reaction between ammonia and oxygen.

(b) Give TWO reasons why excess air is used in the plant to oxidize the ammonia gas.

(c) Why do you think the first stage is operated at atmospheric pressure?

(d) Why do you think the first stage is operated at a temperature of 900 °C?

(e) Why do you think the gases are cooled before the second oxidation?

(f) How will the ratio of dinitrogen tetraoxide to nitrogen dioxide be affected by a rise in temperature? Give a reason.

$$N_2O_4(g) \rightleftharpoons 2NO_2(g); \quad \Delta G^{\ominus}_{450} = -22 \text{ kJ mol}^{-1}$$

(g) State TWO significant factors that a manufacturer should have considered before building a plant to operate at 8 atmospheres throughout.

(Answers on page 109)

Exercise 72 Nitric acid is manufactured from the air together with a suitable source of hydrogen; ammonia is an essential intermediate.

(a) Write the equations, including state symbols, for FOUR chemical reactions which are important in this manufacture of nitric acid. For each reaction give the conditions under which it is carried out.

(b) A sample of gas taken from one stage of the process had the composition, by volume: H_2, 74.2%; N_2, 24.7%; CH_4, 0.8%; Ar, 0.3%; CO, less than 1 part per million. Do you think this would be a suitable general composition for the gas entering the ammonia synthesizer? Explain.

(Answers on page 109)

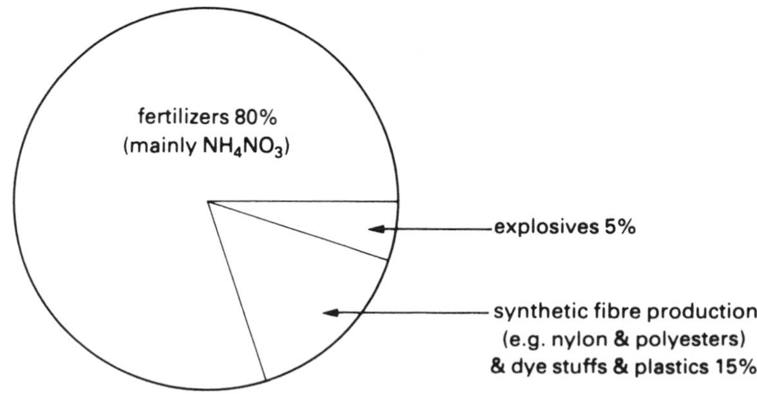

Fig.27. Uses of nitric acid

We now turn our attention from Group V to Group VI, where the most important industrial chemistry concerns the production of sulphuric acid.

The manufacture of sulphuric acid by the contact process

Sulphuric acid is a very important industrial chemical. Many processes require it at some stage of the manufacture. It is used to make fertilizers such as ammonium sulphate and calcium superphosphate, and in the making of explosives, detergents, accumulators, varnishes and artificial fibres such as rayon.

Objectives. When you have finished this section you should be able to:

(67) outline the contact process for the production of sulphuric acid, (full technical details are not required);

(68) state the main sources from which sulphur dioxide is obtained;

(69) explain the choice of temperature and pressure in the contact process;

(70) state the effect of the catalyst on the equilibrium;

(71) list the main uses of sulphuric acid.

You probably already know something about the contact process from your earlier studies, in which case some of the work which follows will be revision. Refer to your notes and/or your textbooks to help you with the next three exercises, the first of which refers to the flow-chart in Fig. 28 below.

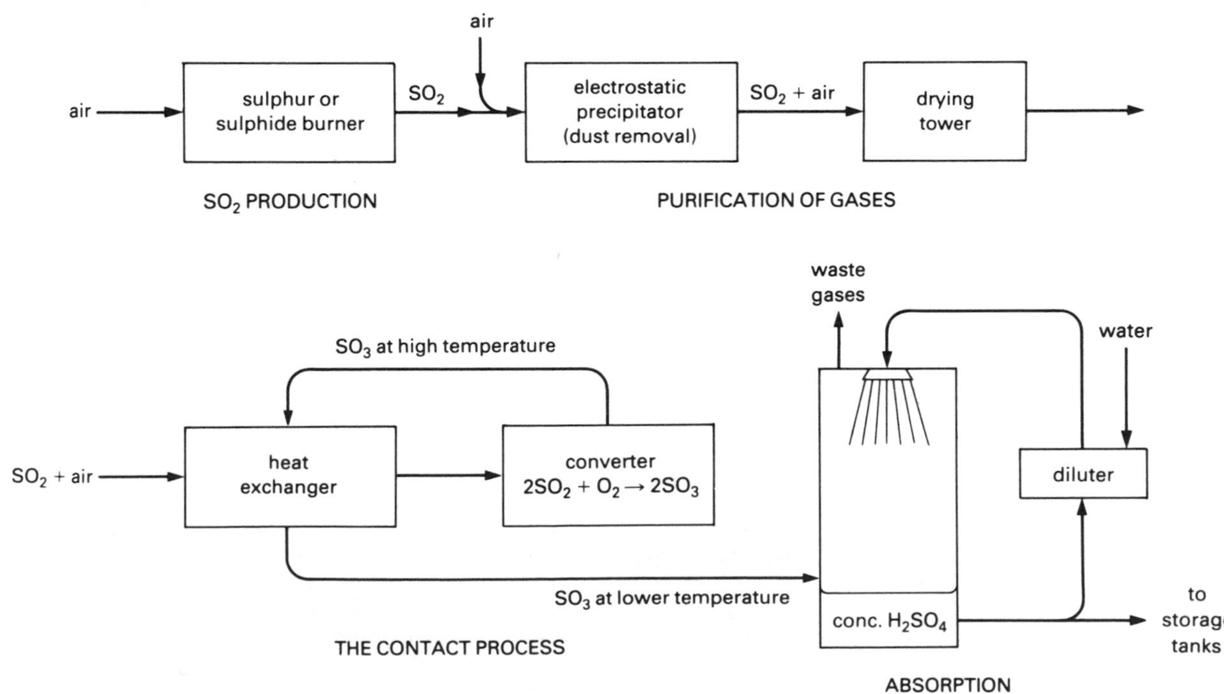

Fig.28. The production of sulphuric acid

Exercise 73

(a) State how sulphur dioxide is obtained from

(i) sulphur (ii) a sulphide.

Give the appropriate equations in your answer.

(b) There have been periods in the past when a significant proportion of the U.K.'s sulphuric acid was manufactured from sulphur extracted from anhydrite, $CaSO_4$, a widely-occurring and easily-obtained mineral. Suggest reasons why this process was introduced and then discarded.

(c) Name the catalyst used in the contact process.

(d) Why is it important to remove impurities from the sulphur dioxide?

(e) Explain why sulphur trioxide is absorbed into concentrated sulphuric acid and then diluted with water rather than absorbed into water immediately. Give any relevant equation.

(f) Why is the sulphur trioxide passed through a heat exchanger?

(Answers on page 110)

In the next exercise you consider the effects of temperature, pressure and a catalyst on the conversion of sulphur dioxide to sulphur trioxide.

Exercise 74

The following equilibrium is involved in the preparation of sulphuric acid by the contact process.

$$2SO_2(g) + O_2(g) \rightleftharpoons 2SO_3(g); \quad \Delta H^{\ominus} = -188 \text{ kJ mol}^{-1}$$

(a) Write the expression for K_p for the above equilibrium.

(b) State the effect on the equilibrium of each of the following changes:

(i) increase of pressure at constant temperature,

(ii) increase of temperature at constant pressure.

Explain your answer in each case.

(c) Give approximate values of the temperature and pressure which are used in the industrial process.

(d) Comment on the pressure used in the industrial process.

(e) A catalyst containing vanadium(V) oxide is used in the process. What is its effect on the conversion of SO_2 to SO_3?

(Answers on page 110)

Now try another A-level question on the contact process.

Exercise 75 (a) Sulphuric acid is manufactured from sulphur by the 'contact' process. Write the equations, including state symbols, for FOUR chemical reactions which are important in this process of manufacture. For each reaction give the conditions under which it is carried out.

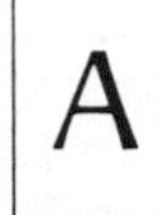

(b) On one occasion a sample of the gas mixture in one part of the plant was analysed and found to consist of SO_2, 10%; SO_3, 0.2%; O_2, 11%; and N_2, 79% by volume.

(i) At what point in the process was the sample taken?

(ii) Does the general composition of the sample indicate that the plant was working properly or not? Explain.

(Answers on page 110)

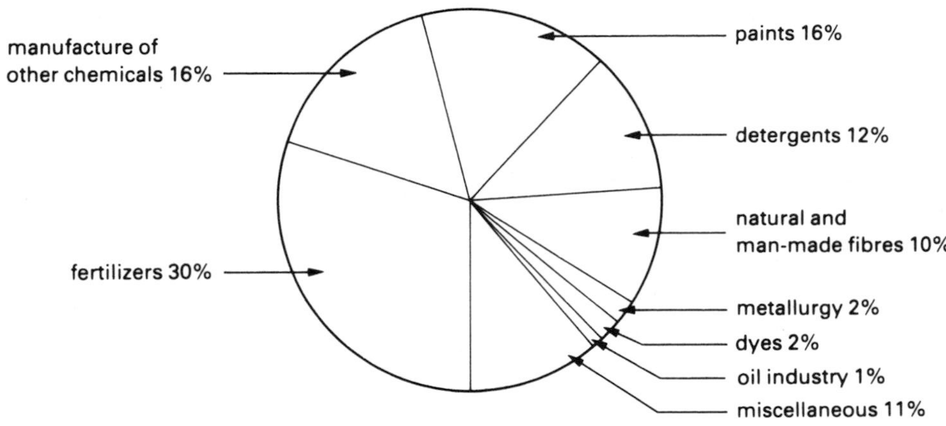

Fig.29. The uses of sulphuric acid

Some aspects of the manufacture of sulphuric acid have been incorporated into an interesting computer program, which you may have used before.

Computer simulation of sulphuric acid manufacture

The Schools Council 'Computers in the Curriculum Project' has produced a program called 'The manufacture of sulphuric acid', which investigates the conflicting demands of best equilibrium yield, high daily production and profitable manufacture. If you did not use this program in Unit P1 (Equilibrium I: Principles), ask your teacher if it is available now.

C

You do not need to know anything about computing but, if you have not used a program before, you will need a few minutes instruction on getting started and using the keyboard. You will need the students' notes which accompany the program, and up to two hours of computing time.

LEVEL TWO CHECKLIST

You have now reached the end of this Unit. If you have studied all the sections, you should have achieved the objectives listed at the end of Level One and, in addition, be able to:

(54) describe how pure aluminium oxide is obtained from bauxite;

(55) & (56) describe how aluminium is extracted from its oxide by electrolysis and explain why this method of extraction is chosen;

(57) explain how and why aluminium is anodized;

(58) list the uses of aluminium and relate these to its properties;

(59) & (60) describe the Haber process for the manufacture of ammonia, stating the sources from which nitrogen and hydrogen are obtained;

(61) & (62) explain the choice of temperature and pressure in the Haber process and state the effect of the catalyst on the equilibrium;

(63) list the main uses of ammonia;

(64) & (65) describe the manufacture of nitric acid and explain the operating conditions by considering Le Chatelier's principle;

(66) list the main uses of nitric acid;

(67) & (68) outline the contact process for the production of sulphuric acid; state the main source of sulphur for the production of sulphur dioxide;

(69) & (70) explain the choice of temperature and pressure in the contact process and state the effect of the catalyst on the equilibrium reaction;

(71) list the main uses of sulphuric acid.

Check that you have adequate notes on the sections you have studied before attempting the End-of-Unit Test.

END-OF-UNIT TEST

To find out how well you have learned the material in this Unit, particularly in Level Two, try the test which follows. Ask your teacher which questions you should attempt.

There is also an End-of-Unit Practical Test (page 82), which is more relevant to Level One and is designed particularly for those students who will take a practical examination. Ideally, you should do this test under examination conditions, so we have not given you a requirements list. There are no special hazard warnings but you should wear safety spectacles for all practical work.

END-OF-UNIT PRACTICAL TEST

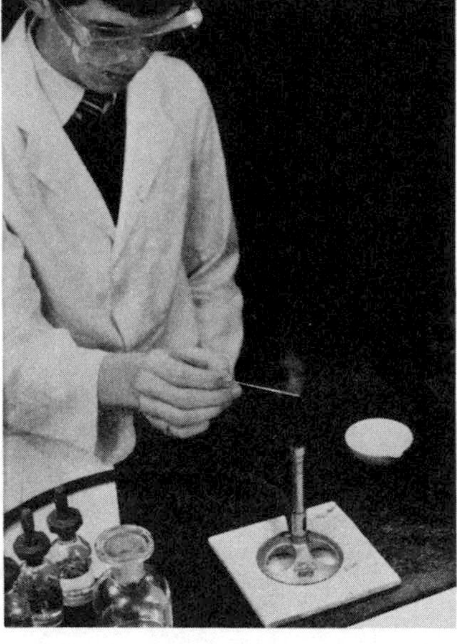

You are provided with aqueous solutions, labelled B, C and D, of three salts. They are compounds of the same three elements.

Carry out the following experiments. Record your observations and inferences in a (larger copy of) the table below, commenting on the types of chemical reactions involved.

A

Results Table 6

Test	Observations	Inferences
1. To 2 or 3 cm³ of solution B add a few drops of dilute hydrochloric acid. Now add a few drops of aqueous barium chloride.		
2. To 2 or 3 cm³ of solution B add a few drops of aqueous lead ethanoate (lead acetate). Now add an excess of aqueous ammonium ethanoate (ammonium acetate) and shake the mixture.		
3. To about 5 cm³ of solution C in a boiling-tube add about 10 cm³ of dilute hydrochloric acid. Allow the mixture to stand for a minute or two. Cautiously smell the mixture. Warm, if necessary, and test the gas evolved. Describe below how you performed this test. Method:		
4. (a) In a small beaker place 2 or 3 cm³ of aqueous copper(II) sulphate. Acidify with two drops of dilute sulphuric acid. Now add about 5 cm of aqueous potassium iodide. (b) To the mixture obtained in 4(a) add solution C until in excess, swirling well.		
5. (a) In a small beaker mix about 2 cm³ of aqueous sodium chloride with an equal volume of aqueous silver nitrate. (b) To the mixture obtained in 5(a) add solution C until in excess, swirling well.		
6. Dissolve about 1 g of iron(II) sulphate crystals in dilute sulphuric acid and add a few drops of aqueous potassium thiocyanate. Now add a few drops of solution D.		
7. (a) In a small beaker place about 5 cm³ of aqueous potassium iodide and a few drops of dilute sulphuric acid. Now add about 5 cm³ of solution D. Warm this mixture. (b) To the mixture obtained in 7(a) add solution C until in excess, swirling well.		
8. Evaporate a small quantity of solution B to dryness and perform a flame test on the residue. Describe below how you do this. Method:		

END-OF-UNIT TEST

1. The following representation indicates a possible series of reactions occurring in the electrolytic extraction of aluminium:

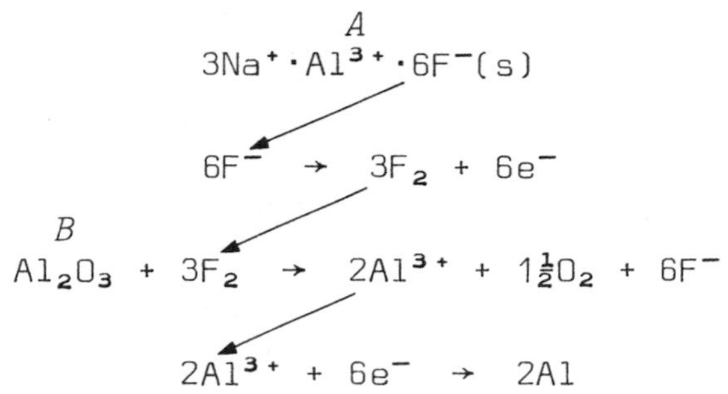

(a) Name the raw materials *A* and *B*. (2)

(b) Write the equation which represents ion discharge at the cathode. (1)

(c) Write the equation which represents ion discharge at the anode. (1)

(d) Which gas is evolved at the anode? (1)

(e) Explain, using these equations, why the aluminium is effectively produced from *B* and not from *A*. (2)

(f) State the nature of the chemical bonds in *B* and so explain why *B* cannot be electrolysed directly. (3)

(g) Explain why fluorine is able to form an ionic compound as in *A*.

(h) Briefly mention the physical conditions under which this electrolysis occurs, naming suitable materials for anode and cathode. (2)

(i) Gallium, Ga, is in the same group of the Periodic Table as aluminium. Complete the equations:

$Ga(s) + 3H^{+}(aq) \rightarrow \ldots(aq) + \ldots(g)$

$Ga(s) + OH^{-}(aq) + H_2O \rightarrow \ldots(aq) + \ldots(g)$

What sort of chemical behaviour for Ga do these equations show? (4)

(j) Write the formula of hydrated potassium gallium sulphate. (2)

(Continued overleaf.)

2. (a) (i) A gaseous system at equilibrium may be represented by the equation:

$$A + B \rightleftharpoons C; \quad \Delta H^{\ominus} = -x \text{ kJ mol}^{-1}$$

What is the effect of a rise in temperature on the equilibrium constant, K_p?

A part

(ii) Immediately following the catalytic oxidation of ammonia in industry, a mixture containing nitrogen oxide (NO) and oxygen emerges from the converter. However, in the laboratory nitrogen oxide, when exposed to the air, is immediately converted into nitrogen dioxide. Suggest an explanation for this difference in behaviour. (5)

(b) By reference to the manufacture of nitric acid from ammonia, state the conditions in the converter of

(i) temperature, (ii) pressure, (iii) catalyst,

and comment briefly on the reasons for their choice. (6)

3. (a) Give the formula of each of the following compounds, and identify the oxidation number of the nitrogen in that compound.

A

(i) nitric acid,

(ii) nitrous acid,

(iii) sodium nitride,

(iv) ammonium iodide,

(v) nitrogen trifluoride. (10)

(b) With reference to the Haber process for the manufacture of ammonia from hydrogen and nitrogen, state

(i) the basic equation for the process,

(ii) whether the reaction is exothermic or endothermic,

(iii) the effect of temperature on the yield of ammonia,

(iv) the effect of temperature on the rate of reaction,

(v) the experimental conditions used in the actual process as carried out in industry. (8)

(c) Give two major uses of ammonia in industry, with sufficient detail to show the chemistry of those uses. (4)

A

4. (a) Give the formula of each of the following compounds, and identify the oxidation number of the sulphur in that compound.

   (i) sulphuric acid,

   (ii) sulphurous acid,

   (iii) barium sulphide,

   (iv) sodium thiosulphate,

   (v) sulphur hexafluoride. (10)

(b) With reference to the manufacture of sulphuric acid from sulphur dioxide by the contact process, state

   (i) the equation for the oxidation reaction involved in the process,

   (ii) whether this reaction is exothermic or endothermic,

   (iii) the effect of temperature on the yield of reaction product,

   (iv) the effect of temperature on the rate of reaction,

   (v) the experimental conditions used in the actual process as carried out industrially. (8)

(c) Give two major applications of sulphuric acid in industry, stating clearly the function of the acid in each application. (4)

(Total 75 marks)

ANSWERS

(Answers to questions from examination papers are provided by ILPAC and not by the Examination Boards.)

Exercise 1

(a) The ore is called bauxite and consists primarily of aluminium oxide (hydrated).

b) Boron is usually encountered as a brown amorphous powder (occasionally as black crystals) with very low conductivity. Aluminium is a silvery grey crystalline metal with high conductivity.

(c) The differences suggest that boron is non-metallic and aluminium is metallic in character.

(d) Assuming that the usual group trend of increasing metallic character continues down the group, we should expect thallium to be metallic in appearance and a good electrical conductor.

Exercise 2

(a) B: $1s^2 2s^2 2p^1$ or $(He)2s^2 2p^1$

Al: $1s^2 2s^2 2p^6 3s^2 3p^1$ or $(Ne)3s^2 3p^1$

(b) Boron and aluminium exhibit the +3 oxidation state.

(c) By analogy with Group IV we might expect the 'inert pair effect' to be observed in Group III also, in which case the possible oxidation states of thallium would be +1 (Tl^+) and +3 (Tl^{3+}).

(d) (i) B^{3+}: 0.016 nm Al^{3+}: 0.045 nm

These are among the smallest ionic radii listed.

(ii) In view of its high charge and very small size, we might expect B^{3+} to polarize any neighbouring anions to such an extent as to make all boron compounds predominantly covalent. The same argument applies to aluminium, but to a lesser extent.

Exercise 3

In comparing two half-reactions, the more negative $E^\ominus$ value favours the oxidation process, and the more positive $E^\ominus$ value favours the reduction process. This is equivalent to the 'anti-clockwise rule', provided the half-equations are written in the same order as they appear in the redox series, i.e. with the more negative $E^\ominus$ value first.

(a)

$$Al^{3+}(aq) + 3e^- \rightleftharpoons Al(s) \qquad E^\ominus = -1.66\ V$$
$$2H^+(aq) + 2e^- \rightleftharpoons H_2(g) \qquad E^\ominus = 0.00\ V$$
$$\Delta E^\ominus = (0.00 - -1.66)\ V = +1.66\ V$$

Aluminium would be expected to react with dilute acids, producing aqueous aluminium ions and hydrogen gas.

(b)

$$Al(OH)_4^-(aq) + 3e^- \rightleftharpoons Al(s) + 4OH^-(aq) \qquad E^\ominus = -2.35\ V$$
$$2H_2O(l) + 2e^- \rightleftharpoons H_2(g) + 2OH^-(aq) \qquad E^\ominus = -0.83\ V$$
$$\Delta E^\ominus = +1.52\ V$$

Aluminium would be expected to react with dilute alkalis, producing aqueous aluminate ions and hydrogen gas.

Experiment 1 Specimen results

Results Table 1 Reactions of aluminium

Reagent	Observations	Identity of any gas given off
Sodium hydroxide solution	Slow evolution of gas at first, becoming quicker.	Hydrogen
Sodium hydroxide solution after immersion in $CuCl_2(aq)$	Rapid evolution of gas.	Hydrogen
Dilute hydrochloric acid	No reaction in cold. Gas evolved on heating.	Hydrogen
Dilute hydrochloric acid after immersion in $CuCl_2(aq)$	Gas evolved in the cold.	Hydrogen
Air after immersion in $CuCl_2(aq)$	No visible reaction.	–
Air after immersion in $HgCl_2(aq)$	White crumbly solid appeared on surface.	–

Results Table 2 Reactions of aluminium solutions

	Observations	
Reagent	Solution of aluminium in sodium hydroxide	Solution of aluminium in dilute hydrochloric acid
Dilute sulphuric acid	A white gelatinous precipitate appeared which dissolved on shaking. More acid made the ppt. permanent and still more redissolved it. The tube became warm.	NONE
Sodium hydroxide solution	NONE	A white gelatinous precipitate appeared which dissolved on shaking. More alkali made the ppt. permanent and still more redissolved it. The tube became warm.
Sodium carbonate solution	NONE	A gas was evolved (CO_2) and a white gelatinous precipitate appeared which dissolved on shaking. More alkali made the ppt. permanent but it did not redissolve. The tube became warm.

Experiment 1 Questions

1. Aluminium is normally covered in a thin invisible layer of aluminium oxide which is not easily removed and protects the metal surface from further attack by air and even by dilute acids. Any oxide formed on the surface of iron does not adhere well enough to protect the metal. (Remember also that $E^{\ominus}$ values refer only to standard conditions.)

2. Solutions of copper(II) chloride and mercury(II) chloride remove the oxide layer and expose the aluminium surface, which then reacts more vigorously with acids and alkalis. (How the oxide layer is removed is not clear. It is interesting to note that the chloride ions play a part - other copper salts are not effective.)

3. Displacement reactions occur with the cations in solution, producing metallic copper and mercury. The copper is simply washed off and the aluminium surface then becomes again covered with a protective layer of oxide. On the other hand, liquid mercury dissolves some aluminium to form an alloy (called an amalgam) which exposes aluminium atoms to attack by oxygen but does not allow a coherent protective layer to form.

4. Washing-soda and many oven-cleaners are alkaline in solution and therefore tend to attack aluminium pans and other kitchenware.

5. (a) For a transfer of 6 electrons,

$$2Al(s) \rightarrow 2Al^{3+}(aq) + 6e^-$$
$$6H^+(aq) + 6e^- \rightarrow 3H_2(g)$$

Adding: $2Al(s) + 6H^+(aq) \rightarrow 2Al^{3+}(aq) + 3H_2(g)$

(b) For a transfer of 6 electrons,

$$2Al(s) + 8OH^-(aq) \rightarrow 2Al(OH)_4^-(aq) + 6e^-$$
$$6H_2O(l) + 6e^- \rightarrow 3H_2(g) + 6OH^-(aq)$$

Adding: $2Al(s) + 2OH^-(aq) + 6H_2O(l) \rightarrow 2Al(OH)_4^-(aq) + 3H_2(g)$

6. The addition of acid first neutralizes excess alkali, allowing a precipitate of aluminium hydroxide to appear. The precipitate dissolves in excess acid.

The addition of sodium hydroxide first neutralizes excess acid, and then a precipitate of aluminium hydroxide appears. The precipitate dissolves in excess alkali to form aluminate ions.

$$Al^{3+}(aq) + 3OH^-(aq) \rightarrow Al(OH)_3(s)$$

$$Al(OH)_3(s) + OH^-(aq) \rightleftharpoons Al(OH)_4^-(aq)$$

The addition of alkali first neutralizes excess acid, and then a precipitate of aluminium hydroxide appears. The precipitate dissolves in excess alkali.

The addition of sodium carbonate first neutralizes excess acid, releasing carbon dioxide. Sodium carbonate is alkaline by hydrolysis:

$$CO_3^{2-}(aq) + H_2O(l) \rightleftharpoons HCO_3^-(aq) + OH^-(aq)$$

so that a precipitate of aluminium hydroxide again appears. However, the concentration of hydroxide ions is never sufficient to redissolve the precipitate.

Exercise 4

(a) Remove the oxide layer by immersing small pieces of aluminium in copper(II) chloride solution. Rinse in water and dissolve in hot dilute sulphuric acid. Reduce the volume of the resulting solution by boiling and allow the solution to cool. Colourless crystals of $Al_2(SO_4)_3 \cdot xH_2O$ separate on cooling.

(b) (i) Relative molecular mass of $Al_2(SO_4)_3 \cdot xH_2O = 54 + 288 + 18x$

$$= 342 + 18x$$

$$\therefore \text{ \% of Al in } Al_2(SO_4)_3 \cdot xH_2O = \frac{54}{342 + 18x} = \frac{8.1}{100}$$

$$\therefore 8.1\ (342 + 18x) = 5400$$

$$2770.2 + 145.8x = 5400$$

$$145.8x = 5400 - 2770.2 = 2629.8$$

$$\therefore x = \frac{2629.8}{145.8} = \boxed{18}$$

(ii) Like other solutions containing non-transition-metal ions, an aqueous solution of $Al_2(SO_4)_3 \cdot xH_2O$ is colourless.

(c) Aluminium does not dissolve readily in dilute acids because the coating of aluminium oxide on its surface protects it. If the coating is removed the aluminium reacts vigorously with dilute acids, as predicted by the strongly negative $E^{\ominus}$ value.

Exercise 5

(a) Boiling-point of BF_3 = 174 K (-99 °C)

Boiling-point of BCl_3 = 286 K (13 °C)

Boiling-point of AlF_3 = 1530 K (1257 °C)

Boiling-point of $AlCl_3$ = 451 K (178 °C)

} These are sublimation temperatures, i.e. at ordinary pressure the transition is solid ⇌ gas

(b) Aluminium fluoride has the greatest ionic character, which is reflected in its high boiling-point. The boiling-points of the other halides are more in line with compounds with a high degree of covalent character.

Aluminium fluoride is more ionic than the other compounds because the Al^{3+} ion is less polarizing than B^{3+}, and because F^- is less polarizable than Cl^-.

(c) In ionic character, $AlF_3 > AlCl_3 > AlBr_3 > AlI_3$

The halide ions increase in size from F^- to I^- and thus become more polarizable. This leads to a much greater degree of covalent character in AlI_3 compared to AlF_3.

Exercise 6

(a) 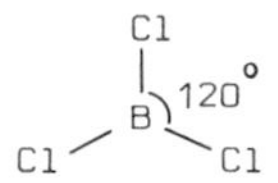 BCl_3: B bonded to three Cl atoms, angle 120° — trigonal planar - all angles 120°

(b) In view of their considerable covalent character, the chlorides of B and Al would be expected to dissolve in organic solvents.

(c) (i) M_r for aluminium chloride at 400 °C is twice that at 800 °C because at 400 °C the molecules in the vapour exist as dimers, Al_2Cl_6, whereas at 800 °C they are completely dissociated into monomers, $AlCl_3$.

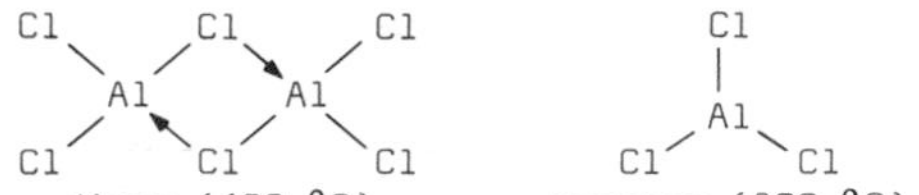

dimer (400 °C)　　monomer (800 °C)

(ii) At 600 °C aluminium chloride vapour consists of the dimer and monomer in dynamic equilibrium with each other.

$$Al_2Cl_6 \rightleftharpoons 2AlCl_3$$

Thus, M_r has a value between that of the dimer and monomer.

(d) The small size of the boron atom does not permit four chlorine atoms to surround it, i.e. steric hindrance prevents the formation of B_2Cl_6 by dative bonding, as in Al_2Cl_6. M_r for boron chloride vapour is always the value for the monomer, BCl_3, i.e. 117.

Exercise 7

(a) $BCl_3(l) + 3H_2O(l) \rightleftharpoons B(OH)_3(aq) + 3HCl(aq)$
boric acid　hydrochloric acid

$AlCl_3(s) + 6H_2O(l) \rightleftharpoons [Al(H_2O)_6]^{3+}(aq) + 3Cl^-(aq)$
hexaaquaaluminium(III) ion　chloride ion

(b) The resulting solutions in both cases are acidic.

(c) BCl_3 is an 'electron-deficient' compound (only six electrons found around B) and can thus form dative covalent bonds with the oxygen atoms in water. This initiates the hydrolysis reaction. On the other hand, CCl_4 is not electron-deficient and cannot form similar dative bonds. (Note that hydrolysis of other Group IV chlorides can occur by the use of d-orbitals which are not available for carbon - see Unit I4.)

(d) 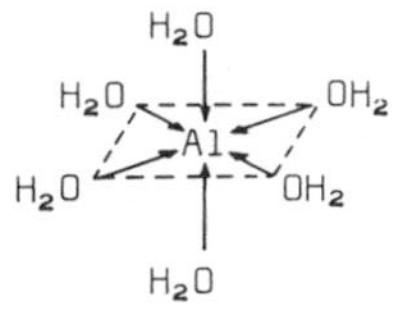 $[Al(H_2O)_6]^{3+}$: Al surrounded by six H_2O ligands. This is an octahedral ion

(e) No d-orbitals are available for boron to form dative bonds with ligands in the way aluminium does. Even if there were, B^{3+} is too small to accommodate six ligands around it.

(f) An alternative molecular formula is H_3BO_3.

Exercise 8

(a) $[Al(H_2O)_6]^{3+}(aq) + H_2O(l) \rightleftharpoons [Al(H_2O)_5(OH)]^{2+}(aq) + H_3O^+(aq)$

$[Al(H_2O)_5(OH)]^{2+}(aq) + H_2O(l) \rightleftharpoons [Al(H_2O)_4(OH)_2]^+(aq) + H_3O^+(aq)$

(b) For $B(OH)_3$, $K_a(298\ K) = 5.8 \times 10^{-10}\ mol\ dm^{-3}$

For $[Al(H_2O)_6]^{3+}$, $K_a(298\ K) = 1.0 \times 10^{-5}\ mol\ dm^{-3}$

$[Al(H_2O)_6]^{3+}$ is a stronger acid than $B(OH)_3$.

(c) In $B(OH)_3$, boron is electron-deficient and can therefore form dative covalent bonds with the oxygen atoms in water.

$$B(OH)_3 + {:}OH_2 \rightleftharpoons [B(OH)_4]^- + H^+(aq)$$

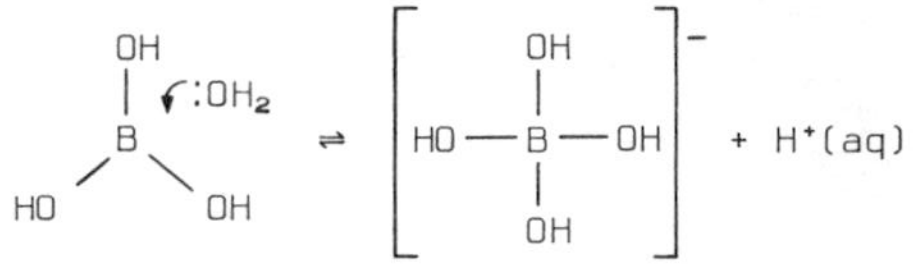

(d) The O—H bond in the hexaaquaaluminium ion is polarized and weakened by the small and highly-charged aluminium ion at the centre of the complex strongly attracting the electrons of the Al—O bonds towards itself. This, in turn, causes the electrons of the O—H bonds to move towards the oxygen atoms and facilitates the loss of protons.

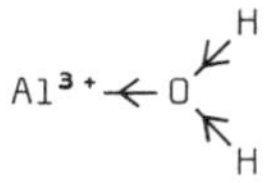

(e) The movement of electrons mentioned in (d) results in a less highly-charged aluminium ion in $[Al(H_2O)_5(OH)]^{2+}$ once the first proton has been released. This reduced charge reduces the polarization of the Al—O bonds. Thus, the O—H bonds in $[Al(H_2O)_5(OH)]^{2+}$ are stronger than in $[Al(H_2O)_6]^{3+}$ and therefore less likely to release protons.

Exercise 9

(a) In the hydrolysis of $[Al(H_2O)_6]^{3+}$ the following equilibria exist:

$[Al(H_2O)_6]^{3+}(aq) + H_2O(l) \rightleftharpoons [Al(H_2O)_5(OH)]^{2+}(aq) + H_3O^+(aq)$

$[Al(H_2O)_5(OH)]^{2+}(aq) + H_2O(l) \rightleftharpoons [Al(H_2O)_4(OH)_2]^+(aq) + H_3O^+(aq)$

In the presence of stronger bases, the above equilibria are displaced over to the right by the removal of the hydronium ion. Furthermore, a base such as sodium carbonate solution is strong enough to remove one more proton from $[Al(H_2O)_4(OH)_2]^+$ forming an insoluble white precipitate of hydrated aluminium hydroxide.

$2[Al(H_2O)_4(OH)_2]^+(aq) + CO_3^{2-}(aq) \rightleftharpoons 2[Al(H_2O)_3(OH)_3](s) + CO_2(g) + H_2O(l)$

(b) In the presence of an excess of strong base, such as aqueous sodium hydroxide, a proton can be removed from each of the coordinated water molecules in $[Al(H_2O)_6]^{3+}$. Thus, if the sodium hydroxide solution is not in excess, a white precipitate of aluminium hydroxide is formed.

$[Al(H_2O)_4(OH)_2]^+(aq) + OH^-(aq) \rightleftharpoons H_2O(l) + [Al(H_2O)_3(OH)_3](s)$
hydrated aluminium hydroxide

But in the presence of excess hydroxide ions, further protons are removed to produce the soluble aluminate(III) ions:

$[Al(H_2O)_3(OH)_3](s) + OH^-(aq) \rightleftharpoons [Al(H_2O)_2(OH)_4]^-(aq) + H_2O(l)$

$[Al(H_2O)_2(OH)_4]^-(aq) + OH^-(aq) \rightleftharpoons [Al(H_2O)(OH)_5]^{2-}(aq) + H_2O(l)$

$[Al(H_2O)(OH)_5]^{2-}(aq) + OH^-(aq) \rightleftharpoons [Al(OH)_6]^{3-}(aq) + H_2O(l)$

Exercise 10

(a)

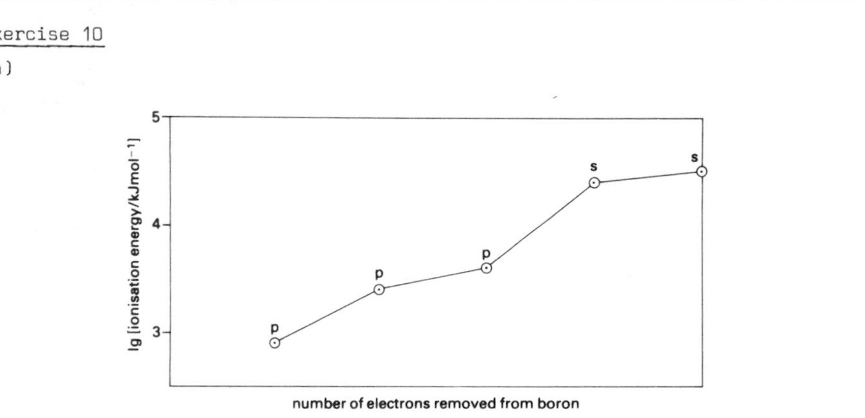

The graph (and the table) show that there are three electrons in the outer shell and, therefore, the most likely formula of boron oxide is B_2O_3.

(b)

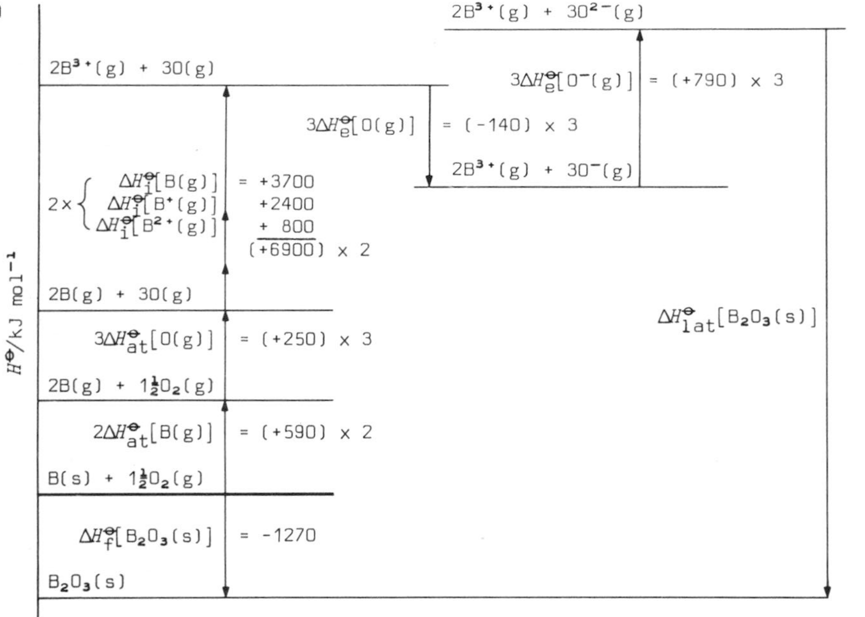

$\Delta H^{\ominus}_{lat}[B_2O_3(s)] = -(1270 + 1180 + 750 + 13800 - 420 + 2370)\ \text{kJ mol}^{-1}$

$= \boxed{-18950\ \text{kJ mol}^{-1}}$

Continued above right.

Exercise 10 (continued)

(c) $B_2O_3(s) + 3H_2O(l) \rightleftharpoons 2H_3BO_3(aq)$ [or $2B(OH)_3(aq)$]

We think that this is the expected equation, but there is, of course, another equilibrium:

$$B(OH)_3(aq) + H_2O(l) \rightleftharpoons [B(OH)_4]^-(aq) + H_3O^+(aq)$$

(d) There is poor agreement because the theoretical derivation assumes that the lattice consists of spherical ions. B^{3+} is so small and highly-charged that it causes extensive distortion of O^{2-} ions leading to a considerable degree of covalent bonding for which the calculation is, at best, an approximation.

Exercise 11

(a)

Oxide	$\Delta H^{\ominus}_f$(298 K) /kJ mol⁻¹	$\Delta G^{\ominus}_f$(298 K) /kJ mol⁻¹
B_2O_3	-1272.8	-1193.7
Al_2O_3	-1675.7	-1582.4

(b) Values of both $\Delta H^{\ominus}_f$ and $\Delta G^{\ominus}_f$ are large and negative, which suggests great stability with respect to decomposition to the elements, especially for aluminium oxide.

Exercise 12

Aluminium oxide is used:

(a) for dehydrating alcohols to the corresponding alkenes;

(b) as the stationary phase in column chromatography;

(c) as an abrasive, in its hard crystalline form (corundum).

Exercise 13

(a) On heating, aluminium sulphate first loses water of crystallization and then decomposes into aluminium oxide and oxides of sulphur, predominantly the trioxide.

$$Al_2(SO_4)_3(s) \rightleftharpoons Al_2O_3(s) + 3SO_3(g)$$

(b) Distortion of the sulphate ion electron cloud by the small, highly-charged aluminium ion leads to the easier decomposition of $Al_2(SO_4)_3$ compared to other sulphates.

(c) Aluminium sulphate is used:

(i) as a mordant in dyeing, i.e. to make dyes more permanent;

(ii) to make waterproof cloth;

(iii) to size paper, i.e. to make it less absorbent;

(iv) to make foam fire-extinguishers;

(v) to precipitate impurities in water supplies and sewage.

Exercise 14

(a) Crystals of potassium aluminium sulphate can be prepared by dissolving equimolar amounts of potassium sulphate and aluminium sulphate in water. The volumes of liquid should then be reduced by evaporation and the solution allowed to cool. Colourless, octahedral crystals appear on cooling.

(b) The general formula of alums is $X^{+}Y^{3+}(SO_4^{2-})_2 \cdot 12H_2O$
(Y is not necessarily Al)

The formula of potassium aluminium sulphate is $KAl(SO_4)_2 \cdot 12H_2O$

(c) The solution would be acidic because the hydrated aluminium ions are hydrolysed just as they are in solutions of simple aluminium salts.

$$[Al(H_2O)_6]^{3+}(aq) + H_2O(l) \rightleftharpoons [Al(H_2O)_5(OH)]^{2+}(aq) + H_3O^{+}(aq)$$

Exercise 15

Table 2

Test	Observations	Equation(s)
1. Flame test (i) $Al_2(SO_4)_3$ (ii) $KAl(SO_4)_2$	No colour. Lilac colour.	
2. Dropwise addition of excess aqueous sodium hydroxide (i) $Al_2(SO_4)_3(aq)$ (ii) $KAl(SO_4)_2(aq)$	For each a white gelatinous ppt. is formed which dissolves in excess to give a colourless solution.	$[Al(H_2O)_6]^{3+}(aq) + 3OH^-(aq) \rightarrow Al(H_2O)_3(OH)_3(s) + 3H_2O(l)$ $Al(H_2O)_3(OH)_3(s) + OH^-(aq) \rightarrow [Al(H_2O)_2(OH)_4]^-(aq) + H_2O(l)$ [Further replacement of H_2O by OH^- is possible.)
3. Addition of aqueous sodium carbonate (i) $Al_2(SO_4)_3(aq)$ (ii) $KAl(SO_4)_2(aq)$	For each a white gelatinous ppt. is formed and effervescence is seen.	$[Al(H_2O)_6]^{3+}(aq) + 3CO_3^{2-}(aq) \rightarrow Al(H_2O)_3(OH)_3(s) + 3HCO_3^-(aq)$ $HCO_3^-(aq) + H^+(aq) \rightarrow H_2O(l) + CO_2(g)$
4. Addition of aqueous barium chloride (i) $Al_2(SO_4)_3(aq)$ (ii) $KAl(SO_4)_2(aq)$	For each a heavy white ppt. is formed.	$Ba^{2+}(aq) + SO_4^{2-}(aq) \rightarrow BaSO_4(s)$

(b) Crystals of both double salts and complex salts contain fixed proportions of the individual ions and molecules from which they are made. However, in a solution of a double salt, these individual species are independent of each other whereas, in a complex salt, some of them are combined together in complex ions. Alums are double salts.

Exercise 16

(a) N: $1s^2 2s^2 2p^3$ P: $1s^2 2s^2 2p^6 3s^2 3p^3$ 5 outer-shell electrons

(b) $:N \vdots N\,$ (dot-and-cross) i.e. $N \equiv N$

(c) White phosphorus - yellowy-white, waxy solid stored under water.
Red phosphorus - violet-red powder.
Black phosphorus - dark grey, flaky solid.

(d) P P P P (60°) White phosphorus. Tetrahedral P_4 molecule.

—P—P—P—P— Red phosphorus. Linked triangles form a long irregular chain.

Red phosphorus, since it is polymeric, has the higher boiling-point.

(e) When heated to 400 °C or above, in the absence of air, red phosphorus sublimes. When the vapour is cooled, white phosphorus is formed.

(f) Bismuth is quite strongly metallic and has a typical metal structure in which Bi^{3+} ions are surrounded by a 'sea' of mobile electrons.

Exercise 17

(a) (i) None of the elements is likely to form the X^{5-} ion. This is because the ions would be too large and highly-charged to be stable. They would be disrupted by internal repulsive forces and/or so extensively polarized by neighbouring cations as to form covalent bonds.

(ii) The element most likely to form the X^{3-} ion is nitrogen. The attraction between the nucleus and incoming electrons is greatest for the nitrogen atom, due to its small size. Furthermore, N^{3-} is least readily polarized, due to its small size.

(iii) The element most likely to form the X^{3+} ion is bismuth. The bismuth atom is the largest in Group 5 and so exerts the weakest attraction for its outer electrons (low ionization energies). The inert pair effect is most evident for elements at the bottom of a group, which leads us to expect Bi^{3+} rather than Bi^{5+}.

(b) X^{3-}: lithium nitride, Li_3N. X^{3+}: bismuth trichloride, $BiCl_3$.

Exercise 18

(a) Nitrogen must be passed through the flask to flush out air which would otherwise react with the phosphine as soon as it is formed.

(b) Phosphine would ignite on contact with air, forming white clouds of oxides of phosphorus.

$$4PH_3(g) + 8O_2(g) \rightarrow P_4O_{10}(s) + 6H_2O(g)$$

(Spontaneous ignition is probably due to the oxidation of impurities such as P_2H_4, but pure phosphine is readily oxidized, sometimes explosively, on gentle heating.)

(c) A sample of phosphine may be collected by placing a test-tube full of water over the delivery tube outlet and allowing the gas to displace the water from the test-tube.

Exercise 19

(a) Table 3

Reagent	Nitrogen	White phosphorus	Red phosphorus
Hydrogen	Forms NH_3 reversibly at high temp. and pressure.	No reaction.	No reaction.
Oxygen	Forms a little NO at very high temp. (e.g. 2000 °C)	Ignites at 35 °C to form P_4O_6 or P_4O_{10}.	Ignites at 260 °C to form P_4O_6 or P_4O_{10}.
Chlorine	No reaction.	Reacts spontaneously to form PCl_3 or PCl_5.	Reacts on heating to form PCl_3 or PCl_5.
Magnesium	Magnesium nitride, Mg_3N_2, formed on heating.	Forms the phosphide, Mg_3P_2, on heating.	Forms the phosphide, Mg_3P_2, on heating.
Alkali	No reaction.	Phosphine, PH_3, formed.	No reaction.
Conc. HNO_3	No reaction.	Explosive reaction to form H_3PO_4.	H_3PO_4 formed.

(b) (i) $P_4(s) + 3OH^-(aq) + 3H_2O(l) \rightarrow 3H_2PO_2^-(aq) + PH_3(g)$
phosphinate ion
(hypophosphite)

(ii) $P_4(s) + 6Mg(s) \rightarrow 2Mg_3P_2(s)$

(Note that P_4 is preferred in equations specifically for white phosphorus, but you may find 4P in some texts for phosphorus in general.)

(c) Red phosphorus does not react with alkalis whereas white phosphorus does. With other reagents, white phosphorus reacts much more vigorously than red, e.g. with air or oxygen. White phosphorus is toxic but red is not.

White phosphorus is more volatile and less dense than red. Unlike the red form, white phosphorus is soluble in some non-polar solvents (e.g. carbon disulphide, CS_2) and it glows in the dark due to slow oxidation.

(d) As previously described, white phosphorus is molecular (P_4) while red phosphorus has a giant structure. This accounts for differences in volatility, density and solubility, and is also related to reactivity. In the P_4 molecule, all the bond angles are 60°, which means that the molecule is 'strained', i.e. the bonding pairs are close together and repel each other fairly strongly. Therefore, less energy is required to disrupt the structure and initiate chemical reactions than in red phosphorus where there is less 'strain'.

Exercise 20

(a) There are six covalent P—P bonds in each P_4 molecule.

(b) (i) $4P(g) \rightarrow P_4(g)$; $\Delta H^\ominus = -(6 \times 201)$ kJ mol^{-1} = **-1206 kJ mol^{-1}**

(ii) $4N(g) \rightarrow N_4(g)$; $\Delta H^\ominus = -(6 \times 163)$ kJ mol^{-1} = **-978 kJ mol^{-1}**

(iii) $4P(g) \rightarrow 2P{\equiv}P(g)$; $\Delta H^\ominus = -(2 \times 488)$ kJ mol^{-1} = **-976 kJ mol^{-1}**

(iv) $4N(g) \rightarrow 2N{\equiv}N(g)$; $\Delta H^\ominus = -(2 \times 945)$ kJ mol^{-1} = **-1890 kJ mol^{-1}**

(c) The calculations above show that the formation of P_4 and N_2 molecules is energetically more favourable than the formation of P_2 and N_4 molecules. Similar calculations show that As_4 and Sb_4 are more likely than As_2 and Sb_2.

P_2 molecules would be likely to convert to P_4 molecules:

$$2P_2(g) \rightarrow P_4(g); \quad \Delta H^\ominus = (-1206 + 976) \text{ kJ mol}^{-1} = -230 \text{ kJ mol}^{-1}$$

N_4 molecules would be even more likely to convert to N_2 molecules:

$$N_4(g) \rightarrow 2N_2(g); \quad \Delta H^\ominus = (-1890 + 978) \text{ kJ mol}^{-1} = -912 \text{ kJ mol}^{-1}$$

(d) Nitrogen atoms are much smaller than phosphorus atoms. Consequently, singly-occupied *p*-orbitals are able to overlap to a greater extent in N_2 molecules, giving very strong π-bonding.

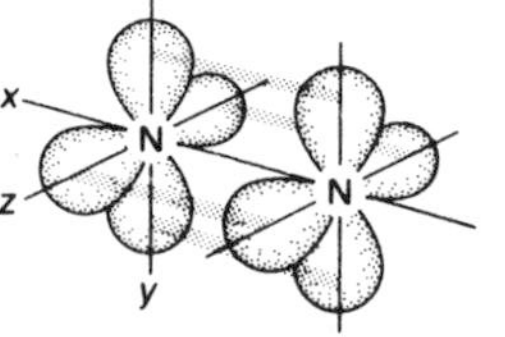

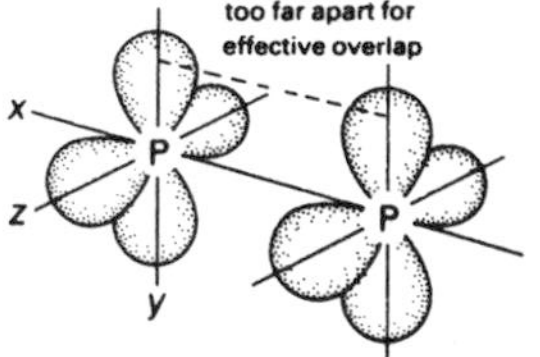

(e) Bonds must be broken before reaction can occur. It requires far less energy to break a P-P bond than it does to break a N≡N bond (even from N≡N to N=N). This is one reason why phosphorus is more reactive.

Exercise 21

Nitrogen consists of diatomic molecules, each containing a triple bond, N≡N.

Molecular phosphorus, i.e. the white allotrope, consists of P_4 molecules in which each atom is linked to three others by single bonds.

The relative affinities of nitrogen and phosphorus for oxygen and chlorine are illustrated below:

$N_2(g) + O_2(g) \rightleftharpoons 2NO(g)$ (High temperature only. Small yield.)

$N_2(g) + Cl_2(g)$ (No reaction.)

$P_4(s) + 3O_2(g) \rightarrow P_4O_6(s)$ (Ignites at 35 °C. Some P_4O_{10} also.)

$P_4(s) + 6Cl_2(g) \rightarrow 4PCl_3(l)$ (Spontaneous at room temperature. Some PCl_5.)

The reaction of nitrogen with oxygen (and a possible reaction with chlorine) involves breaking N≡N bonds, which requires very much more energy than breaking P—P bonds in the reactions of phosphorus. This could account for the greater reactivity of phosphorus, assuming that similar amounts of energy are released in the formation of products in each case.

Exercise 22

(a) (i) The amount of phosphorus atoms used = $\frac{0.31\ \text{g}}{31\ \text{g mol}^{-1}}$ = **0.01 mol**

(ii) The amount of Cu produced = $\frac{1.60\ \text{g}}{64\ \text{g mol}^{-1}}$ = **0.025 mol**

(iii) 0.01 mol of P deposits 0.025 mol of Cu

∴ 1 mol of P deposits **2.5 mol of Cu**

(b) (i) The oxidation state of Cu in $CuSO_4$ is +2 and the oxidation state of elemental Cu is 0.

∴ the change in oxidation number is **from +2 to 0**

(ii) From the results above we have:

$1P(s) + 2\frac{1}{2}CuSO_4(aq) \rightarrow 2\frac{1}{2}Cu(s)$ + acidic soln containing P

∴ $2P(s) + 5CuSO_4(aq) \rightarrow 5Cu(s)$ + acidic soln containing P

For the process: $5Cu^{2+} \rightarrow 5\ Cu$,

the change in ox. no. = 5 x (-2) = -10

∴ two P atoms must change by +5 each, from 0 to **+5**

(iii) In HPO_n, $Ox(\text{H}) + Ox(\text{P}) + (Ox(\text{O}) \times n) = 0$

i.e. $1 + 5 - 2n = 0$ ∴ n = **3**

(c) $2P(s) + 5CuSO_4(aq) + 6H_2O(l) \rightarrow 5Cu(s) + 2HPO_3(aq) + 5H_2SO_4(aq)$ or

$P_4(s) + 10CuSO_4(aq) + 12H_2O(l) \rightarrow 10Cu(s) + 4HPO_3(aq) + 10H_2SO_4(aq)$

(d) (i) At room temperature, the phosphorus will smoulder and possibly catch fire. Apart from the hazard involved, the mass of the phosphorus is likely to change during weighing.

(ii) Weigh a beaker containing the copper(II) sulphate solution. Using forceps, remove the phosphorus from its storage water and drop it into the solution. Weigh the beaker again - the increase in mass is equal to the mass of phosphorus (plus a drop or two of water). For greater accuracy, the phosphorus could be dried quickly in a jet of nitrogen or other unreactive gas.

Exercise 23

(a) Covalent bonds are formed by sharing of unpaired electrons. Both nitrogen and phosphorus have three unpaired electrons, in $2p$-and $3p$-orbitals respectively, and might be expected to form three covalent bonds in the chlorides NCl_3 and PCl_3.

In phosphorus, promotion of an electron is possible from the $3s$-orbital into a $3d$ orbital to give five unpaired electrons, which allows the formation of five covalent bonds in compounds such as PCl_5. The promotion energy, 1370 kJ mol^{-1}, can be recovered in the formation of the additional bonds.

In nitrogen, however, there are no $2d$-orbitals and the formation of five covalent bonds would involve promotion from the $2s$-to a $3s$-orbital. The energy requirement for this is too great to be feasible.

(b) Solid PCl_5 exists as $PCl_4^+PCl_6^-$.

Exercise 24

(a) $\Delta H^{\ominus}_f[NCl_3(l)] = +230.1$ kJ mol^{-1}; $\Delta H^{\ominus}_f[PCl_3(l)] = -319.7$ kJ mol^{-1}

(b) $\frac{1}{2}N_2(g) + \frac{3}{2}Cl_2(g) \rightarrow NCl_3(l)$; $\Delta H^{\ominus} = +230.1$ kJ mol^{-1}

$P(s) + \frac{3}{2}Cl_2(g) \rightarrow PCl_3(l)$; $\Delta H^{\ominus} = -319.7$ kJ mol^{-1}

(c) The $\Delta H^{\ominus}_f$ values suggest that $NCl_3(l)$ is unstable wheras $PCl_3(l)$ is stable with respect to decomposition to their elements. In practice, NCl_3 is dangerously explosive.

Exercise 25

$NCl_3(l) + 3H_2O(l) \rightarrow NH_3(aq) + 3HClO(aq)$
ammonia chloric(I) acid

$PCl_3(l) + 3H_2O(l) \rightarrow H_2PHO_3(aq)^* + 3HCl(aq)$
phosphonic acid hydrochloric acid

$PCl_5(s) + H_2O(l) \rightarrow PCl_3O(l) + 2HCl(aq)$
phosphorus trichloride oxide

$PCl_3O(l) + 3H_2O(l) \rightarrow H_3PO_4(aq) + 3HCl(aq)$
phosphoric(V) acid

*Phosphonic acid is still often called phosphorous acid and given the formula H_3PO_3. The formula H_2PHO_3 is preferred since it shows that the acid is dibasic, the third hydrogen being attached directly to the phosphorus.

H—P(=O)(—OH)—OH

Exercise 26

(a) Cl_2P—Cl + :OH_2 → [Cl_2P(Cl)←OH_2] → Cl_2P—O—H + Cl—H

(b) (HO)P(:OH)—OH → O=P(H)(OH)—OH

(c) Hydrolysis of nitrogen trichloride cannot proceed by a similar mechanism because there are no vacant d orbitals available on the nitrogen atom to make possible the formation of a dative bond between O and N.

(d) H—O—H + NCl_3 → H—O—Cl + H—NCl_2

Exercise 27

(a) If concentrated hydrochloric acid is added to the equilibrium mixture

$$SbCl_3(aq) + H_2O(l) \rightleftharpoons SbClO(s) + 2HCl(aq)$$

the white precipitate will dissolve as the equilibrium is displaced to the left.

(b) The hydrolysis of bismuth trichloride will also be incomplete and it will form a white precipitate of bismuth(III) chloride oxide.

$$BiCl_3(aq) + H_2O(l) \rightleftharpoons BiClO(s) + 2HCl(aq)$$

(c) Aqueous solutions of $SbCl_3$ and $BiCl_3$ contain added concentrated HCl(aq) to prevent the precipitation of chloride-oxides by hydrolysis.

Exercise 28

(a)

N N

F F

(b) The molecule N_2F_2 exhibits geometrical isomerism.

F–N=N–F (both F on the same side) *cis*-dinitrogen difluoride

F–N=N–F (F on opposite sides) *trans*-dinitrogen difluoride

Both molecules are planar.

N_2F_2 exhibits this type of isomerism because there is restricted rotation about the N=N bond. Therefore, the two forms are distinct isomers which cannot readily be converted one to the other.

Exercise 29

(a) See above right

(b) The order of increasing thermal stability for the oxides of nitrogen under standard conditions may be deduced from values of $\Delta G_f^{\ominus}$ as follows:

$N_2O_3 < N_2O_5 < N_2O < N_2O_4 < NO < NO_2$

(Values of $\Delta H_f^{\ominus}$ give a different order. Even if you have not studied ΔG in any depth, you should know that values of $\Delta G^{\ominus}$ are more reliable than those of $\Delta H_f^{\ominus}$ in predicting likely reactions. In this case, the reactions are decompositions to the elements.)

(c) The stabilities of N_2O_3 and N_2O_5 go against the general rule that the +3 and +5 oxidation states are dominant in Group V. Note that these oxides are even more unstable with respect to reactions other than decomposition to the elements:

$$N_2O_3 \rightarrow NO + NO_2$$

$$2N_2O_5 \rightarrow 4NO_2 + O_2$$

(d) P_4O_{10} is more stable than P_4O_6.

Exercise 29

(a) Table 4

Oxidation state of N or P		+1	+2	+3	+4		+5
Oxides of nitrogen	Formula	N_2O	NO	N_2O_3	NO_2 ⇌	N_2O_4	N_2O_5
	Common name	Nitrous oxide	Nitric oxide	Nitrogen trioxide	Nitrogen dioxide	Nitrogen tetroxide	Nitrogen pentoxide
	Recommended name	Dinitrogen oxide	Nitrogen monoxide	Dinitrogen trioxide	Nitrogen dioxide	Dinitrogen tetraoxide	Dinitrogen pentoxide
	$\Delta H_f^{\ominus}(\Delta G_f^{\ominus})$ /kJ mol^{-1}	+82 (+104)	+90 (+87)	+84 (+139)	+33 (+51)	+9 (+98)	-43 (+114)
Oxides of phosphorus	Formula			P_4O_6	P_4O_8		P_4O_{10}
	Common name			Phosphorus trioxide	(This oxide is rarely met.)		Phosphorus pentoxide
	Recommended name			Phosphorus (III) oxide	Phosphorus(IV) oxide		Phosphorus (V) oxide
	$\Delta H_f^{\ominus}(\Delta G_f^{\ominus})$ /kJ mol^{-1}			-1640 (—)			-2984 (-2698)

Exercise 30

(a) (i) Nitrogen monoxide is a colourless gas at room temperature.

(ii) Nitrogen dioxide is a dark brown gas at about 30 °C.

(iii) Dinitrogen tetraoxide is a pale yellow liquid at about 5 °C.

(b) (i) Nitrogen monoxide is prepared by the action of moderately concentrated nitric acid (i.e. 50% concentrated acid and 50% water) on copper turnings at room temperature. The gas is collected over water partly to prevent mixing with the air and partly to dissolve any NO_2 which may also be produced.

$$3Cu(s) + 8HNO_3(aq) \rightarrow 3Cu(NO_3)_2(aq) + 4H_2O(l) + 2NO(g)$$

(ii) Nitrogen dioxide is prepared by the action of concentrated nitric acid on copper turnings at room temperature (can be warmed to speed up reaction) and the gas is collected by downward delivery in gas jars.

$$Cu(s) + 4HNO_3(aq) \rightarrow Cu(NO_3)_2(aq) + 2H_2O(l) + 2NO_2(g)$$

Any nitrogen monoxide also formed during the reaction will immediately combine with the oxygen in the air to form nitrogen dioxide.

$$2NO(g) + O_2(g) \rightarrow 2NO_2(g)$$

(iii) Dinitrogen tetraoxide is also produced by reacting concentrated nitric acid with copper but the gas produced (i.e. NO_2) is passed through an ice-cold U-tube where a pale yellow liquid condenses.

$$Cu(s) + 4HNO_3(aq) \rightarrow Cu(NO_3)_2(aq) + 2H_2O(l) + N_2O_4(l)$$

(c) At -10 °C, N_2O_4 is a colourless solid. On heating, it gradually changes to a yellow liquid. At 21 °C, the liquid boils, forming a light brown gas which becomes darker as the temperature increases. Above about 450 °C, the colour becomes progressively paler again until at 600 °C the gas is almost colourless.

At -10 °C, the solid consists of N_2O_4 molecules but the brown gas at about 450 °C consists mostly of NO_2 molecules. At temperatures between -10 °C and 450 °C, the two species are in equilibrium with the proportion of NO_2 increasing as the temperature rises.

$$N_2O_4(g) \rightleftharpoons 2NO_2(g)$$

At about 500 °C, over half the NO_2 decomposes to form nitrogen monoxide and oxygen and at 600 °C most of the gas consists of a colourless mixture of these two gases.

$$2NO_2(g) \rightleftharpoons 2NO(g) + O_2(g)$$

Exercise 31

(a) P_4O_6 is prepared by burning white phosphorus in a limited supply of air. In practice, this can be done by passing a slow current of air over gently-heated phosphorus. The vapour formed is passed through a filter plug of glass wool to remove any solid P_4O_{10}. The remaining vapour is then passed through an ice-cold container where P_4O_6 condenses as a white crystalline solid.

P_4O_{10} is formed by burning white phosphorus in a plentiful supply of oxygen. It can be freed from any P_4O_6 also formed by heating it and passing the vapour with a stream of oxygen over a hot platinized asbestos catalyst.

(b) In molecules of P_4, P_4O_6 and P_4O_{10} all the phosphorus atoms appear at the corners of a tetrahedron.

The P_4O_6 molecule has a 'bridging' oxygen atom between each pair of phosphorus atoms.

The P_4O_{10} molecule consists of a P_4O_6 unit with an additional oxygen atom attached to each phosphorus atom.

(c) $P_4O_6(s) + 2O_2(g) \rightarrow P_4O_{10}(s)$
phosphorus(V) oxide

Exercise 32

Nitrogen monoxide, NO, has an odd number of outer-shell electrons in each molecule. Consequently, its structure cannot be represented by allocating electrons to bonding pairs and non-bonding pairs. The molecule can be regarded as a resonance hybrid of three 'canonical' forms:

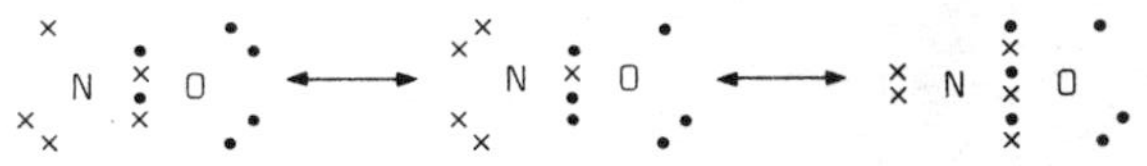

$\bullet N{=}O \longleftrightarrow N{=}O\bullet \longleftrightarrow N{\equiv}O\bullet$

Alternatively, one may say that the electrons are delocalized to give the equivalent of a 'five-electron bond', N$\equiv$O.

Either model is in harmony with the fact that the bond length is intermediate between N=O and N≡O, and is slightly polar - the oxygen atom contributes more of its electron cloud to the bond and is left with a partial positive charge relative to the nitrogen.

Continued overleaf.

Exercise 32 (continued)

Nitrogen dioxide, NO_2, is also an 'odd-electron' molecule. Its structure can be regarded as a resonance hybrid of two canonical forms:

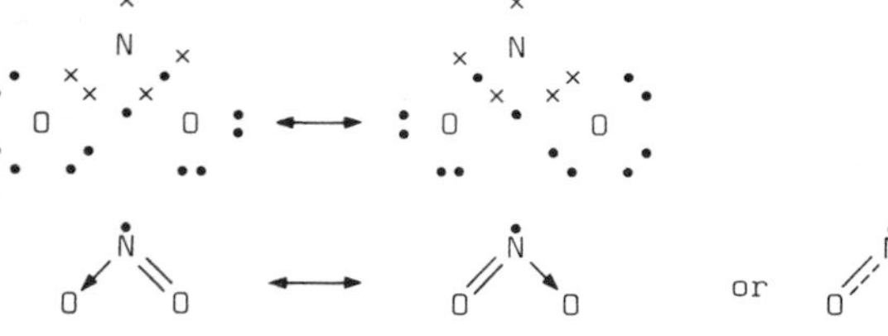

The length of each bond is intermediate between N—O and N=O.

Dinitrogen tetroxide, N_2O_4, has an even number of electrons per molecule: accordingly the structure may be represented by electron pairs. Nevertheless, to account for the fact that all the nitrogen-oxygen bonds are equal in length (intermediate between N—O and N=O), it is necessary to propose a resonance hybrid of canonical forms as before.

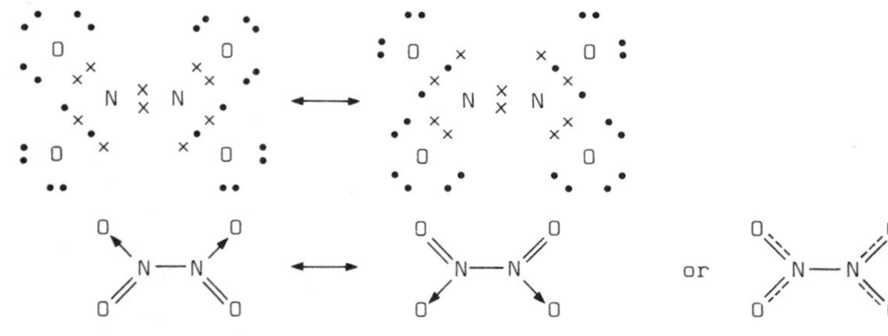

Exercise 33

(a) Single NO_2 molecules are odd-electron molecules. When they dimerize the odd electrons pair up producing a more stable structure (N_2O_4).

(b) NO is an odd-electron molecule so it might be expected to dimerize, forming a more stable structure.

(c) When NO reacts with Cl_2, the odd-electron from NO might be expected to pair up with the odd-electron from a Cl atom forming NOCl.

$$2NO(g) + Cl_2(g) \rightarrow 2NOCl(g)$$

(d) By analogy with the transition metal ions, odd-electron molecules might be expected to be paramagnetic (drawn into a magnetic field) and possibly coloured. (Both NO and NO_2 are paramagnetic; NO_2 is strongly coloured.)

(e) The odd electrons may be lost to form NO^+ (nitrosyl cation) and NO_2^+ (nitryl cation or nitronium ion).

(You have already met the latter in the nitration of benzene, etc.)

Exercise 34

Table 5

Reactant	N_2O	NO	NO_2
Cl_2	No reaction.	NOCl formed in the presence of charcoal.	NO_2 is oxidized to HNO_3 if moist.
Metal, e.g. Cu or Fe	N_2O reduced to N_2 by hot metal.	NO reduced to N_2 by red-hot metal.	NO_2 reduced to N_2 (possibly via NO) by hot metal.
$Fe^{2+}(aq)$	No reaction.	Brown complex $[Fe(H_2O)_5(NO)]^{2+}$ is formed.	Fe^{2+} oxidized to Fe^{3+}.
Glowing splint	Glowing splint is re-lit.	No reaction.	No reaction.
H_2O	Soluble in cold, far less so in hot. No reaction.	Sparingly soluble. No reaction.	Mixture of nitric and nitrous acids formed.

(b) Order of oxidizing ability is: N_2O and NO $<$ NO_2.

(c) N_2O is sometimes called 'laughing gas' and is used as an anaesthetic, particularly in dentistry.

(d) The brown $[Fe(H_2O)_5NO]^{2+}$ complex forms the basis of the brown ring test for nitrates in which concentrated sulphuric acid is added slowly, without mixing, to a solution containing Fe^{2+} ions and the suspected nitrate. The nitrate and the acid react to form a trace of NO which then combines with Fe^{2+} at the junction of the two layers.

(e) (i) Both NO and NO_2 might be expected to decolorize an acidified solution of manganate(VII).

In comparing two half-reactions, the more negative value of $E^{\ominus}$ favours the oxidation process. When the equations are written in the same order as they appear in the redox series, i.e. with increasing $E^{\ominus}$ values, this is equivalent to the 'anti-clockwise rule'.

$$NO_3^-(aq) + 2H^+(aq) + e^- \rightleftharpoons NO_2(g) + H_2O(l); \quad E^{\ominus} = +0.80\ V$$
$$MnO_4^-(aq) + 8H^+(aq) + 5e^- \rightleftharpoons Mn^{2+}(aq) + 4H_2O(l); \quad E^{\ominus} = +1.51\ V$$

$$NO_3^-(aq) + 4H^+(aq) + 3e^- \rightleftharpoons NO(g) + 2H_2O(l); \quad E^{\ominus} = +0.96\ V$$
$$MnO_4^-(aq) + 8H^+(aq) + 5e^- \rightleftharpoons Mn^{2+}(aq) + 4H_2O(l); \quad E^{\ominus} = +1.51\ V$$

Continued on page 96.

Exercise 34 (continued)

(e) (ii) The overall equations may be obtained by adding the half-equations in such a way that the same number of electrons are used in one as are produced in the other.

5 x (reverse of equation 1) + (equation 3) gives:

$5NO_2 + 5H_2O + MnO_4^- + 8H^+ + 5e^- \rightarrow 5NO_3^- + 10H^+ + 5e^- + Mn^{2+} + 4H_2O$

which simplifies to:

$$5NO_2(g) + H_2O(l) + MnO_4^-(aq) \rightarrow 5NO_3^-(aq) + 2H^+(aq) + Mn^{2+}(aq)$$

5 x (reverse of equation 2) + 3 x (equation 3) gives:

$5NO + 10H_2O + 3MnO_4^- + 24H^+ + 15e^- \rightarrow 5NO_3^- + 20H^+ + 15e^- + 3Mn^{2+} + 12H_2O$

which simplifies to:

$$5NO(g) + 3MnO_4^-(aq) + 4H^+(aq) \rightarrow 5NO_3^-(aq) + 3Mn^{2+}(aq) + 2H_2O(l)$$

(f) A strongly-glowing splint provides sufficient energy to decompose some dinitrogen oxide into nitrogen and oxygen.

$2N_2O(g) \rightarrow 2N_2(g) + O_2(g)$

The increase in the proportion of oxygen present is sufficient to relight the splint.

(g) Reactions with chlorine

$2NO(g) + Cl_2(g) \rightleftharpoons 2NOCl(g)$

$NO_2(g) + \frac{1}{2}Cl_2(g) + H_2O(l) \rightarrow HNO_3(l) + HCl(g)$

Reactions with metals

$N_2O(g) + Cu(s) \rightarrow CuO(s) + N_2(g)$

$3N_2O(g) + 2Fe(s) \rightarrow Fe_2O_3(s) + 3N_2(g)$

$2NO(g) + 2Cu(s) \rightarrow 2CuO(s) + N_2(g)$

$6NO(g) + 4Fe(s) \rightarrow 2Fe_2O_3(s) + 3N_2(g)$

$2NO_2(g) + 4Cu(s) \rightarrow 4CuO(s) + N_2(g)$

$6NO_2(g) + 8Fe(s) \rightarrow 4Fe_2O_3(s) + 3N_2(g)$

You may also find: $2Cu(s) + NO_2(g) \rightarrow Cu_2O(s) + NO(g)$ (lower temp.)

Reactions with $Fe^{2+}(aq)$

$NO(g) + [Fe(H_2O)_6]^{2+}(aq) \rightarrow [Fe(H_2O)_5(NO)]^{2+}(aq) + H_2O(l)$

$NO_2(g) + 2Fe^{2+}(aq) + 2H^+(aq) \rightarrow NO(g) + 2Fe^{3+}(aq) + H_2O(l)$ (also the reaction above)

Reaction with water

$2NO_2(g) + H_2O(l) \rightarrow HNO_2(aq) + HNO_3(aq)$

Exercise 35

(a) (i) $P_4O_6(s) + 6H_2O(l) \rightarrow 4H_2PHO_3(aq)$ phosphonic acid [or $4H_3PO_3(aq)$ phosphorous acid]

(ii) $P_4O_{10}(s) + 6H_2O(l) \rightarrow 4H_3PO_4(aq)$ phosphoric(V) acid

(b) P_4O_{10} is hydrolysed more readily.

(c) Phosphorus(V) oxide is used as a powerful drying agent and as a dehydrating agent in organic chemistry, e.g. in the conversion of amides to nitriles.

$RCONH_2 \rightarrow RCN + H_2O$

(d) The oxides of Group V in the +3 oxidation state might be expected to vary from acidic at the top via amphoteric to basic at the bottom. This is in accordance with the usual increase in metallic character as the group is descended (nitrogen is a non-metal; bismuth is a metal).

Exercise 36

(a) (i) There are two half-reactions involving nitrous acid. In combining these, the more negative $E^\ominus$ value favours the oxidation process (right to left as written) and the more positive $E^\ominus$ value favours the reduction process (left to right). Therefore, nitrous acid might be expected to disproportionate:

$NO_3^-(aq) + 3H^+(aq) + 2e^- \rightleftharpoons HNO_2(aq) + H_2O(l)$; $E^\ominus = +0.94$ V

$HNO_2(aq) + H^+(aq) + e^- \rightleftharpoons NO(g) + H_2O(l)$; $E^\ominus = +0.99$ V

The overall equation is given by reversing the first equation and adding twice the second:

$HNO_2 + H_2O + 2HNO_2 + 2H^+ + 2e^- \rightleftharpoons NO_3^- + 3H^+ + 2e^- + 2NO + 2H_2O$

which simplifies to:

$3HNO_2(aq) \rightleftharpoons NO_3^-(aq) + 2NO(g) + H^+(aq) + H_2O(l)$; $\Delta E^\ominus = +0.05$ V

Although $\Delta E^\ominus$ is small, the equilibrium shifts to the right as NO escapes into the air and reacts with oxygen.

(ii) As the pH is lowered, $[H^+(aq)]$ increases. This shifts the equilibrium to the left, i.e. the nitrous acid becomes more stable.

(b) Iodine, nitrogen monoxide and water.

$I_2(aq) + 2e^- \rightleftharpoons 2I^-(aq)$; $E^\ominus = +0.54$ V

$HNO_2(aq) + H^+(aq) + e^- \rightleftharpoons NO(g) + H_2O(l)$; $E^\ominus = +0.99$ V

(c) Bromide ions, nitrate ions and hydrogen ions.

$NO_3^-(aq) + 3H^+(aq) + 2e^- \rightleftharpoons HNO_2(aq) + H_2O(l)$; $E^\ominus = +0.94$ V

$Br_2(aq) + 2e^- \rightleftharpoons 2Br^-(aq)$; $E^\ominus = +1.09$ V

(d) In (b), nitrous acid acts as an oxidizing agent (electron acceptor). In (c), nitrous acid acts as a reducing agent (electron donor).

(e) (i) Nitrous acid would be expected to oxidize iodide to iodine as in (b) but would have no effect on bromide. The likely products are iodine, nitrogen monoxide and water.

(ii) The lower organic layer would turn purple due to the released iodine dissolving in the tetrachloromethane.

Exercise 37

(a) HNO_3: $Ox(N) = - Ox(H) - 3Ox(O) = -1 + 6 = \boxed{+5}$

HNO_2: $Ox(N) = - Ox(H) - 2Ox(O) = -1 + 4 = \boxed{+3}$

NO_3^-: $Ox(N) = \text{charge} - 3Ox(O) = -1 + 6 = \boxed{+5}$

NO_2^-: $Ox(N) = \text{charge} - 2Ox(O) = -1 + 4 = \boxed{+3}$

(b) In nitric acid and nitrates, nitrogen is in its highest possible oxidation state. The oxidation states of hydrogen and oxygen rarely change. Therefore, we would not expect nitric acid or nitrates to be oxidized (behave as reducing agents) but they could be reduced (behave as oxidizing agents).

In nitrous acid and nitrites, nitrogen is in oxidation state +3. Since there are common nitrogen compounds with oxidation states higher and lower than this we might expect nitrous acid to behave both as a reducing agent and an oxidizing agent.

(c) (i) $\overset{+5}{HNO_3}, \overset{+5}{NO_3^-} \leftrightarrow \overset{+4}{NO_2} \leftrightarrow \overset{+3}{HNO_2}, \overset{+3}{NO_2^-} \rightarrow \overset{+2}{NO} \rightarrow \overset{+1}{N_2O} \rightarrow \overset{0}{N_2} \rightarrow \overset{-3}{NH_3}, \overset{-3}{NH_4^+}$

(ii) Lists of standard electrode potentials show half equations involving the compounds listed. By comparing their $E^\ominus$ values with those of other oxidizing agents and reducing agents, it is possible to check whether particular redox reactions are energetically feasible.

Experiment 2 Specimen results

Results Table 3 Reactions of nitric acid and nitrates

Reactants		Observations	Identity of gas
1. Copper and	16 M HNO_3	Rapid evolution of red-brown gas. Tube became hot. Green solution formed.	Nitrogen dioxide, NO_2
2. Copper and	8 M HNO_3	Slow bubbling. Gas was colourless near solution, red-brown near mouth of tube. Solution turned blue.	Nitrogen monoxide, NO. Then NO → NO_2
3. Magnesium and	2 M HNO_3	Rapid bubbling. Gas was brownish but also popped with a lighted splint.	Nitrogen dioxide and hydrogen, NO_2 and H_2
4. Magnesium and	0.5 M HNO_3	Slow bubbling. Gas was colourless and popped with a lighted splint.	Hydrogen, H_2
5. Devarda's alloy and a nitrate in alkali.		Rapid bubbling. Gas was colourless, popped with a lighted splint and turned red litmus paper blue.	Hydrogen and ammonia, H_2 and NH_3.
6. Aluminium foil and a nitrate in alkali.		Slow bubbling at first, then faster. Gas was colourless, flammable and turned red litmus paper blue.	Hydrogen and ammonia, H_2 and NH_3.

Note that the reaction of nitric acid with a metal always gives a <u>mixture</u> of gaseous products, e.g. NH_3, N_2, N_2O, NO, NO_2, H_2 (and N_2H_4, NH_4^+). One product may be predominant under particular conditions. Mg appears to be the only metal to give H_2 but the 'pop' test may not always work in the presence of other gases.

Results Table 4 Reactions of nitrous acid and nitrites

Reactants in solution	Observations	Identity of coloured product(s)	Oxidation or reduction of NO_2^-
7. Sodium nitrite and sulphuric acid	Solution turned blue. Slow effervescence to give brownish gas.	HNO_2 or perhaps N_2O_3. Gas = NO_2	None. Oxidation.
8. Warm nitrous acid	Blue colour disappeared. Rapid bubbling. Gas was colourless near solution, brown near mouth of tube.	NO_2 (from NO + O_2)	Oxidation (and reduction - see Q.4).
9. Potassium iodide and nitrous acid	Brown solution formed and black precipitate. Trace of brownish gas.	Iodine (I_2 & I_3^-) NO_2	Reduction
10. Potassium manganate(VII) & nitrous acid	Solution became colourless. (Trace of brown ppt. which then cleared.)	(MnO_2 due to local deficiency of acid.)	Oxidation
11a. Iron(II) sulphate & sodium hydroxide	Green precipitate formed.	$Fe(OH)_2$	None
11b. Iron(II) sulphate, nitrous acid & sodium hydroxide	Mixture turned black, then gave a yellow solution. Addition of alkali gave a red-brown ppt.	$Fe(H_2O)_5(NO)^{2+}$ Fe^{3+} $Fe(OH)_3$	None Reduction None
12. Aluminium and a nitrite in alkali	Rapid bubbling. Gas was colourless, popped with a lighted splint and turned red litmus blue.	None	Reduction

Experiment 3. Questions

1. <u>Concentrated nitric acid:</u>

$$Cu(s) + 4HNO_3(aq) \rightarrow Cu^{2+}(aq) + 2NO_3^{2-}(aq) + 2NO_2(g) + 2H_2O(l)$$

The red-brown gas is nitrogen dioxide, NO_2. The blue-green solution is concentrated aqueous copper nitrate.

<u>Moderately concentrated nitric acid:</u>

$$3Cu(s) + 8HNO_3(aq) \rightarrow 3Cu^{2+}(aq) + 6NO_3^{2-}(aq) + 2NO(g) + 4H_2O(l)$$

The blue solution is dilute aqueous copper nitrate. The colourless gas is nitrogen monoxide, NO, which reacts with oxygen in the air to produce nitrogen dioxide, NO_2.

$$2NO(g) + O_2(g) \rightarrow 2NO_2(g)$$

Experiment 3. Questions (continued)

2. The reaction between magnesium and very dilute nitric acid is a simple electron transfer beteen metal and hydrogen, as occurs with other dilute acids.

$$Mg(s) + 2H^+(aq) \rightarrow Mg^{2+}(aq) + H_2(g)$$

At higher concentrations of acid, the combination of nitrate and hydrogen ions becomes a more powerful oxidant than hydrogen ions alone and is reduced by the magnesium to give water and oxides of nitrogen.

3. The main reason is probably that the finely-divided alloy presents a greater surface area for reaction than the aluminium foil. Another reason may be that the alloy is not protected initially by a coherent film of aluminium oxide.

4. $$3HNO_2(aq) \rightarrow H^+(aq) + NO_3^-(aq) + 2NO(g) + H_2O(l)$$

This reaction is an example of disproportionation. The oxidation state of nitrogen both increases and decreases, i.e. it changes from +3 to +5 and +2. Nitric acid cannot undergo disproportionation because the oxidation state of nitrogen is already at its maximum value of +5.

5. (a) Both nitrates and nitrites in alkaline solution react with aluminium or Devarda's alloy to produce ammonia. (Ammonium salts, of course, react similarly but can easily be recognised because ammonia is produced by the action of alkali alone.)

(b) Nitrates do not react with dilute sulphuric acid. Nitrites do react to produce nitrogen monoxide, which immediately combines with oxygen to give red-brown fumes of nitrogen dioxide.

Exercise 38

(a) Amount of Fe $= \dfrac{0.8\text{ g}}{56\text{ g mol}^{-1}} = \dfrac{1}{70}$ mol

Amount of HNO_3 $= \dfrac{0.9\text{ g}}{63\text{ g mol}^{-1}} = \dfrac{1}{70}$ mol

∴ molar ratio of Fe : HNO_3 is 1:1

(b) $$1Fe(s) + 1\ HNO_3(aq) \rightarrow 1Fe^{3+}(aq) + \begin{bmatrix} N_2O \\ \text{or } NO \\ \text{or } N_2O_4 \end{bmatrix}$$

(+3e⁻ from Fe to HNO_3; −3e from Fe)

(c) Nitrogen in HNO_3 is in the +5 oxidation state. If the nitric acid gains three electrons, the final oxidation state of the nitrogen must be +2.

∴ the oxide produced must be **NO**

(d) $1Fe(s) - 3e^- \rightarrow 1Fe^{3+}(aq)$

$3H^+(aq) + 1HNO_3(aq) + 3e^- \rightarrow 1NO(g) + 2H_2O(l)$

Addition of these two equations gives the overall equation:

$$\boxed{Fe(s) + 3H^+(aq) + HNO_3(aq) \rightarrow Fe^{3+}(aq) + NO(g) + 2H_2O(l)}$$

Exercise 39

(a) $H_3PO_4(aq) + OH^-(aq) \rightleftharpoons H_2PO_4^-(aq) + H_2O(l)$
dihydrogenphosphate(V) ion

$H_2PO_4^-(aq) + OH^-(aq) \rightleftharpoons HPO_4^{2-}(aq) + H_2O(l)$
hydrogenphosphate(V) ion

$HPO_4^{2-}(aq) + OH^-(aq) \rightleftharpoons PO_4^{3-}(aq) + H_2O(l)$
phosphate(V) ion

(b) A solution of trisodium phosphate would be strongly alkaline due to hydrolysis. The reactions shown in (a) occur, especially the third one.

$$PO_4^{3-}(aq) + H_2O(l) \rightleftharpoons HPO_4^{2-}(aq) + OH^-(aq)$$

(c) The H_3PO_4 molecule is essentially tetrahedral, as shown in the diagram. The ions are similar in shape, with O atoms successively replacing OH groups.

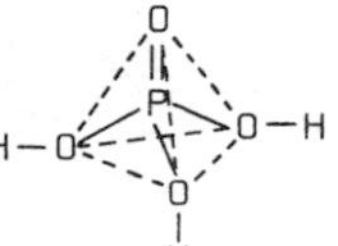

(d) Extensive hydrogen bonding occurs because each molecule contains three hydrogen atoms attached to electronegative atoms and four oxygen atoms capable of forming such bonds.

(e) Phosphoric(V) acid is non-volatile, which makes it suitable for displacing volatile acids from their salts. Unlike concentrated sulphuric acid, it is non-oxidizing, so that hydrogen bromide can be obtained without oxidation to bromine.

$$2KBr(s) + H_3PO_4(l) \rightleftharpoons 2HBr(g) + K_2HPO_4(s)$$

(f) Phosphoric(V) acid may be preferred in order to prevent side-reactions such as oxidation and excessive dehydration (leading to 'charring').

Exercise 40

Table 6 Some reactions of aqueous phosphates

Reagent in solution	Observations	Equation
Silver nitrate	Yellow ppt.	$3Ag^+(aq) + PO_4^{3-}(aq) \rightarrow Ag_3PO_4(s)$
Barium chloride	White ppt.	$3Ba^{2+}(aq) + 2PO_4^{3-}(aq) \rightarrow Ba_3(PO_4)_2(s)$
Iron(III) chloride	Yellowish ppt.	$Fe^{3+}(aq) + PO_4^{3-}(aq) \rightarrow FePO_4(s)$

[Note that, although $PO_4^{3-}(aq)$ is extensively hydrolysed to $HPO_4^{2-}(aq)$, precipitation reactions nearly always involve $PO_4^{3-}(aq)$ since the resulting salts are generally the least soluble. However, most of them are soluble in dilute acids, which helps to distinguish them from other precipitates.]

(b) A small quantity of the solution is warmed gently with a large excess of ammonium molybdate solution in dilute nitric acid. If a phosphate is present, there will be a yellow precipitate (of ammonium phosphomolybdate).

[You can see why a large excess of reagent is needed by looking at the formula of the precipitate, $(NH_4)_3PO_4Mo_{12}O_{36}$, but don't worry about memorising it!]

Exercise 41

(a) Calcium phosphate is too insoluble to be used directly as a commercial fertilizer.

(b) (i) Calcium phosphate can be converted to the superphosphate by treating it with 70% sulphuric acid.

$$Ca_3(PO_4)_2(s) + 2H_2SO_4(aq) \rightarrow Ca(H_2PO_4)_2(s) + 2CaSO_4(s)$$

(ii) Calcium phosphate can be converted to the triplephosphate by treating it with phosphoric acid.

$$Ca_3(PO_4)_2(s) + 4H_3PO_4(aq) \rightarrow 3Ca(H_2PO_4)_2(s)$$

(c) Triplephosphate contains the same amount of calcium as superphosphate but three times the amount of phosphate ion - hence the name.

Exercise 42

(a) In XH_3, $Ox(X) = -3$ (X = a Group V element)
In X_2H_4, $Ox(X) = -2$

(b) The PH_3 molecule would be expected to be similar in shape to NH_3, i.e. trigonal pyramidal:

(c) Phosphorus is less electronegative than nitrogen and has a larger atomic radius. For both these reasons, the bonding pairs in PH_3 are further from the 'centre' of the molecule than they are in NH_3. Consequently, there is less repulsion between them and the bond angle is smaller.

(d) The angle between sp^3-orbitals is $109\frac{1}{2}°$ (tetrahedral). The angle between p-orbitals is 90°. Molecules formed by overlap of these orbitals might be expected to have bond angles close to these values.

Exercise 43

(a)

Hydride :	NH_3	PH_3	AsH_3	SbH_3
Boiling-point/K:	240	183	218	256

(b) With the exception of ammonia, the boiling-points of the XH_3 hydrides increase with increasing relative molecular mass.

(c) The electronegativity of nitrogen is high enough to allow hydrogen bonding to occur between ammonia molecules. The electronegativity of phosphorus is too low for hydrogen bonding to occur between phosphine molecules. The increased intermolecular forces between NH_3 molecules result in an abnormally high boiling-point.

(d) Ammonia molecules can form hydrogen bonds with water molecules whereas phosphine molecules cannot do this to any appreciable extent. Thus, ammonia dissolves in water but phosphine does not.

Exercise 44

(a)
$$2NH_3(g) \rightleftharpoons N_2(g) + 3H_2(g)$$
$$4PH_3(g) \rightleftharpoons P_4(g) + 6H_2(g)$$

(b) Table 8

Bond	Mean bond energy/kJ mol^{-1}
N—H	388
P—H	322
As—H	292
Sb—H	255
Bi—H	Not listed

(c) The bond energy terms in Table 7 do show that less energy is required for bond breaking in the hydrides as the group is descended but this is not sufficient to account for the decreasing thermal stability. The energy released in bond-making must also be considered in order to give values of $\Delta H^\ominus$ for the reactions. However, even $\Delta H^\ominus$ values are not completely reliable indicators of the relative ease with which reactions are likely to occur. Values of $\Delta G^\ominus$ should be compared, and these take into account the variations not only in $\Delta H^\ominus$ but also in entropy due to the varying structures of the products.

Exercise 45

(a) Ammonia is much more basic than phosphine.

(b) A pair of electrons in an sp^3-orbital is much more likely to interact with hydrogen to form a dative bond, i.e. accept a proton, than a pair in an s-orbital because of the different shapes of the orbitals. In an sp^3-orbital, the electron cloud is already localised in a suitable direction for bond formation and projects further from the central nucleus. In other words, the non-bonding pair in a phosphine molecule is less readily available than in ammonia, which makes phosphine less basic.

(c) Since phosphine forms dative bonds less readily than ammonia, the phosphonium ion, PH_4^+, is less stable than the ammonium ion, NH_4^+. An additional factor is that the P—H bond is weaker than the N—H bond; this also contributes to the lower stability of PH_4^+.

Exercise 46

(a) $PH_3(g) + HCl(g) \rightleftharpoons PH_4Cl(s)$ phosphonium chloride

(b) $PH_4I(s) \rightleftharpoons PH_3(g) + HI(g)$

(c) $PH_4I(s) + H_2O(l) \rightarrow PH_3(g) + I^-(aq) + H_3O^+(aq)$

$PH_4I(s) + OH^-(aq) \rightarrow PH_3(g) + I^-(aq) + H_2O(l)$

(d) Similar reactions occur for ammonium salts, but much less readily; complete hydrolysis requires heating with alkali.

(e) The shape of the PH_4^+ ion is tetrahedral, like NH_4^+. All the bond angles are $109\frac{1}{2}°$. (Presumably, sp^3 hybridization must occur here but less readily.)

Exercise 47

(a) Ammonia forms ammine complexes with $Cu^{2+}(aq)$ and $Ag^{+}(aq)$ solutions.

$Cu^{2+}(aq) + 4NH_3(aq) \rightarrow [Cu(NH_3)_4]^{2+}(aq)$

$Ag^{+}(aq) + 2NH_3(aq) \rightarrow [Ag(NH_3)_2]^{+}(aq)$

(Several complexes are known, $[Ag(NH_3)_x]^{+}$, where x has values from 1 to 4, but 2 is the usual number.)

Solutions of $Cu^{2+}(aq)$ and $Ag^{+}(aq)$ are reduced to the phosphide and finally to the metal by phosphine:

$PH_3(g) + 3Cu^{2+}(aq) + 3H_2O(l) \rightarrow 3Cu(s) + H_3PO_3(aq) + 6H^{+}(aq)$

$PH_3(g) + 6Ag^{+}(aq) + 3H_2O(l) \rightarrow 6Ag(s) + H_3PO_3(aq) + 6H^{+}(aq)$

(b) From the reaction in (a) it is clear that ammonia is by far a better complexing agent than phosphine. This is because the lone pair of electrons on the nitrogen atom of the ammonia molecule is far more likely to form dative bonds than the lone pair of electrons on the phosphorus atom in the phosphine molecule. (See also Exercise 45.)

Exercise 48

(a) Ammonia will reduce both oxygen and chlorine under the following conditions:

It will burn in oxygen but not air unless heated to very high temperatures.

$4NH_3(g) + 3O_2(g) \rightarrow 2N_2(g) + 6H_2O(g)$

It will reduce excess chlorine to give the dangerously explosive nitrogen trichloride.

$NH_3(g) + 3Cl_2(g) \rightarrow NCl_3(l) + 3HCl(g)$

If excess ammonia is used, then nitrogen and ammonium chloride are formed.

$2NH_3(g) + 3Cl_2(g) \rightarrow N_2(g) + 6HCl(g)$

$6HCl(g) + 6NH_3(g) \rightarrow 6NH_4Cl(s)$

Phosphine burns readily in air to give phosphorus(V) oxide. Ignition is spontaneous in the presence of the impurity diphosphane, P_2H_4.

$PH_3(g) + 8O_2(s) \rightarrow P_4O_{10}(s) + 6H_2O(g)$

It also ignites spontaneously in chlorine to give phosphorus trichloride.

$PH_3(g) + 3Cl_2(g) \rightarrow PCl_3(l) + 3HCl(g)$

Phosphine reacts far more vigorously than ammonia with oxygen and chlorine. This illustrates the greater reducing power of phosphine.

(b) N—H bonds are stronger than P—H bonds. There is, therefore, a greater energy barrier to overcome in those reactions which require breaking of these bonds.

(c) Ammonia reduces hot copper(II) oxide to copper and is itself oxidized to nitrogen.

$3CuO(s) + 2NH_3(g) \rightarrow 3Cu(s) + 3H_2O(g) + N_2(g)$

Exercise 49

(a) Rhombic sulphur (α-sulphur) is formed as yellow octahedral crystals. Monoclinic sulphur (β-sulphur) has yellow needle-shaped crystals.

Both oxygen, O_2, and trioxygen (ozone), O_3, are colourless gases.

(b) Both allotropes of sulphur are composed of S_8 molecules packed together in different ways. Each S_8 molecule possesses a puckered-ring structure in which the S atoms are linked by single bonds.

The oxygen molecule is linear, with a double bond linking the two atoms.

The trioxygen molecule is angular with an order of $1\frac{1}{2}$ for each bond.

S_8: [puckered ring of eight S atoms]

O_3: O=O—O (angular) ; [resonance structures O=O→O ↔ O←O=O]

O_2: O=O

(c)

	Reactions of sulphur	Reactions of oxygen
(i)	$2Na(s) + S(s) \rightarrow Na_2S(s)$ sodium sulphide	$2Na(s) + O_2(g) \rightarrow Na_2O_2(s)$ sodium peroxide
(ii)	$Fe(s) + S(s) \rightarrow FeS(s)$ iron(II) sulphide	$2Fe(s) + 3O_2(g) \rightarrow 2Fe_2O_3(s)$ iron(III) oxide
(iii)	$H_2(g) + S(s) \rightarrow H_2S(g)$ hydrogen sulphide	$2H_2(g) + O_2(g) \rightarrow 2H_2O(l)$ water
(iv)	$C(s) + 2S(s) \rightarrow CS_2(l)$ carbon disulphide	$C(s) + O_2(g) \rightarrow CO_2(g)$ carbon dioxide $C(s) + \frac{1}{2}O_2(g) \rightarrow CO(g)$ carbon monoxide

Exercise 50

(a) (i) $S_8(g) \rightarrow 4S_2(g)$

Bonds broken: $8\overline{E}(S—S) = (8 \times 264)\ kJ\ mol^{-1} = 2112\ kJ\ mol^{-1}$

Bonds made: $4\overline{E}(S{=}S) = (4 \times 431)\ kJ\ mol^{-1} = 1724\ kJ\ mol^{-1}$

$\therefore \Delta H^{\ominus} = (+2112 - 1724) kJ\ mol^{-1} = \boxed{+388\ kJ\ mol^{-1}}$

(ii) $O_8(g) \rightarrow O_2(g)$

Bonds broken: $8\overline{E}(O—O) = (8 \times 142)\ kJ\ mol^{-1} = 1136\ kJ\ mol^{-1}$

Bonds made: $4\overline{E}(O{=}O) = (4 \times 498)\ kJ\ mol^{-1} = 1992\ kJ\ mol^{-1}$

$\therefore \Delta H^{\ominus} = (+1136 - 1992)\ kJ\ mol^{-1} = \boxed{-856\ kJ\ mol^{-1}}$

(b) The positive $\Delta H^{\ominus}$ value for the change in (a) (i) suggests that the single bonds in the S_8 molecule are not likely to break in order to form S=S double bonds. The high negative $\Delta H^{\ominus}$ value for the change in (a) (ii) suggests that single bonds in a hypothetical O_8 molecule would be very likely to break in order to form O=O double bonds. Thus, O=O bonds are energetically favourable with respect to O—O bonds and S—S bonds are energetically favourable with respect to S=S bonds.

Exercise 51

(a)

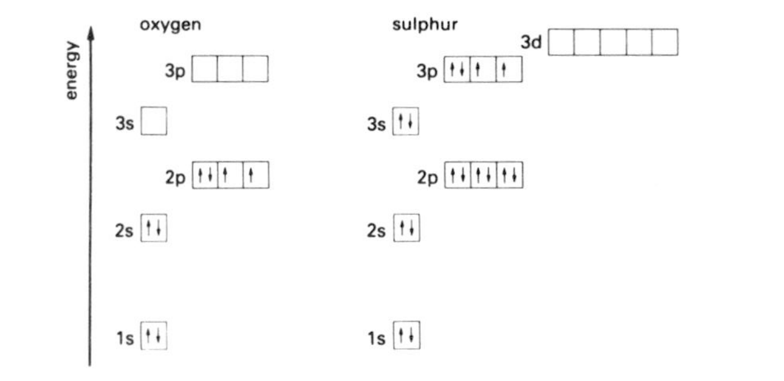

(b) Each atom has two unpaired electrons which can be shared to form two covalent bonds or lost to form doubly-charged ions.

(c) The apparent covalency of oxygen in H_3O^+ is 3. Two of the bonds in H_3O^+ are covalent bonds and the third is a dative covalent bond.

(d) Sulphur can accept two electrons in order to fill its $3p$-orbitals. Since the $3d$-orbitals are so close in energy to the $3p$-orbitals these also can be used in bonding. The availability of the five $3d$-orbitals allows sulphur to exhibit a wide range of oxidation states in its compounds, as shown in the diagram below.

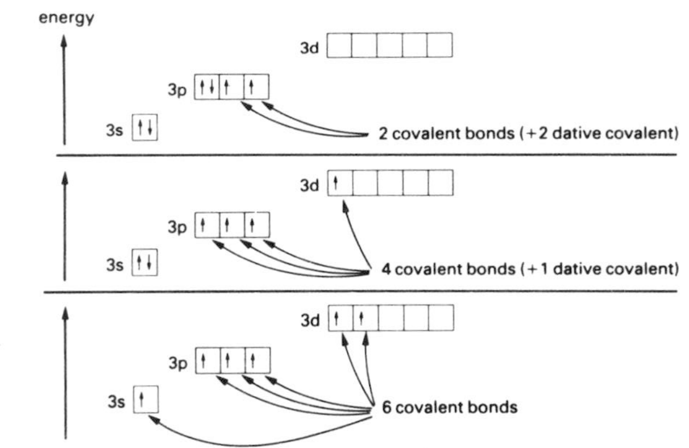

(e) The $3s$ and $3p$-orbitals in oxygen are not available for bonding because of the great difference in energy between them and the $2p$-orbitals.

(f) This effect is called the 'inert pair' effect and it can be seen in the heavier elements of Groups III, IV, V and VI.

Exercise 52

(a) By considering relative molecular masses, hydrogen sulphide would be expected to have a higher boiling-point than H_2O since H_2S molecules have more electrons available to form stronger van der Waals bonds.

(b) Water has a much higher boiling-point than hydrogen sulphide because hydrogen bonds exist between water molecules, and these are much stronger than van der Waals bonds. Hydrogen sulphide cannot form hydrogen bonds because sulphur is not sufficiently electronegative.

Exercise 53

The H_2S molecule has an angular structure because it contains two lone pairs and two bonding pairs of electrons. Mutual repulsion of the electron pairs forces them into approximately tetrahedral positions.

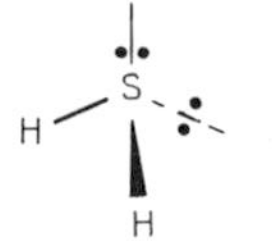

Exercise 54

(a)

	$\Delta H_f^{\ominus}$/kJ mol^{-1}	$\Delta G_f^{\ominus}$/kJ mol^{-1}
$H_2O(g)$	-242	-229
$H_2S(g)$	-20.2	-33.0

These values suggest that it might be easier to produce water than hydrogen sulphide from the elements.

(In fact, hydrogen combines reversibly to a slight extent when passed through molten sulphur near its boiling-point whereas hydrogen and oxygen combine explosively when ignited.)

(b) $\overline{E}(O-H)$ = 463 kJ mol^{-1} $\overline{E}(S-H)$ = 338 kJ mol^{-1}

(c) Water is more thermally stable than hydrogen sulphide because considerably more energy is required to break the O—H bonds in water compared to the S—H bonds in hydrogen sulphide.

(d) $2H_2S(g) + 3O_2(g) \rightarrow 2H_2O(l) + 2SO_2(g)$

Exercise 55

(a) Half-reactions 1 and 2 show hydrogen sulphide and water behaving as reducing agents (donating electrons). Since the more negative value of $E^{\ominus}$ always favours the reducing process, it follows that hydrogen sulphide is the more powerful reducing agent (under standard conditions).

(b) (i)

	$E^{\ominus}/V$
$S(s) + 2H^+(aq) + 2e^- \rightleftharpoons H_2S(aq)$	+0.14
$Fe^{3+}(aq) + e^- \rightleftharpoons Fe^{2+}(aq)$	+0.77

$H_2S(aq)$ should reduce $Fe^{3+}(aq)$ $\Delta E^{\ominus} = +0.63$ V

(ii)

	$E^{\ominus}/V$
$S(s) + 2H^+(aq) + 2e^- \rightleftharpoons H_2S(aq)$	+0.14
$MnO_4^-(aq) + 8H^+(aq) + 5e^- \rightleftharpoons Mn^{2+}(aq) + 4H_2O(l)$	+1.51

$H_2S(aq)$ should reduce $MnO_4^-(aq)$ $\Delta E^{\ominus} = +1.37$ V

(iii)

	$E^{\ominus}/V$
$S(s) + 2H^+(aq) + 2e^- \rightleftharpoons H_2S(aq)$	+0.14
$SO_2(aq) + 4H^+(aq) + 4e^- \rightleftharpoons S(s) + 2H_2O(l)$	+0.45

$H_2S(aq)$ should reduce $SO_2(aq)$ $\Delta E^{\ominus} = +0.31$ V

(iv)

	$E^{\ominus}/V$	
$S(s) + 2H^+(aq) + 2e^- \rightleftharpoons H_2S(aq)$	+0.14	(1)
$SO_4^{2-}(aq) + 4H^+(aq) + 2e^- \rightleftharpoons SO_2(aq) + 2H_2O(l)$	+0.17	(2)

$H_2S(aq)$ should reduce sulphuric acid but, under standard conditions, the reaction would not proceed very far because $\Delta E^{\ominus}$ is so small (0.03 V). However, the use of concentrated sulphuric acid would force equilibrium (2) further to the right and make the reduction more likely under these conditions.

(v)

	$E^{\ominus}/V$
$S(s) + 2H^+(aq) + 2e^- \rightleftharpoons H_2S(aq)$	+0.14
$\frac{1}{2}Cl_2(aq) + e^- \rightleftharpoons Cl^-(aq)$	+1.36

$H_2S(aq)$ should reduce $Cl_2(aq)$ $\Delta E^{\ominus} = +1.22$ V

(c) (i) $2Fe^{3+}(aq) + H_2S(aq) \rightarrow 2Fe^{2+}(aq) + 2H^+(aq) + S(s)$

(ii) $2MnO_4^-(aq) + 6H^+(aq) + 5H_2S(aq) \rightarrow 2Mn^{2+}(aq) + 8H_2O(l) + 5S(s)$

(iii) $SO_2(aq) + 2H_2S(aq) \rightarrow 2H_2O(l) + 3S(s)$

(iv) $H_2SO_4(l) + H_2S(g) \rightarrow SO_2(g) + 2H_2O(l) + S(s)$

(v) $Cl_2(aq) + H_2S(aq) \rightarrow 2HCl(aq) + S(s)$

Exercise 56

(a) In the first ionization stage, H_2S is acting as the acid and H_2O the base. In the second ionization stage, HS^- is acting as the acid and H_2O the base.

(b) Since H_2S is only moderately soluble, $[H_2O(l)] > [H_2S(aq)]$. Since K_1 is very small, $[H_2S(aq)] \gg [HS^-(aq)]$. Since K_2 is very small, $[HS^-(aq)] \gg [S^{2-}(aq)]$. As a result of the first ionization, $[H_3O^+(aq)] = [HS^-(aq)]$, but more H_3O^+ ions are produced by the second ionization, and from water, so that $[H_3O^+(aq)] > [HS^-(aq)]$. Combining these conclusions gives:

$$[H_2O(l)] > [H_2S(aq)] \gg [H_3O^+(aq)] > [HS^-(aq)] \gg [S^{2-}(aq)]$$

Exercise 57

(a) (i) Sodium hydrosulphide, NaHS, is formed when hydrogen sulphide is in excess.

(ii) Sodium sulphide, Na_2S, is formed when sodium hydroxide is in excess.

(b) (i) $NaOH(aq) + H_2S(aq) \rightarrow NaHS(aq) + H_2O(l)$

(ii) $2NaOH(aq) + H_2S(aq) \rightarrow Na_2S(aq) + 2H_2O(l)$

(c) Sodium sulphide solution is alkaline due to hydrolysis of sulphide ions.

$$S^{2-}(aq) + H_2O(l) \rightleftharpoons HS^-(aq) + OH^-(aq)$$

Further hydrolysis can occur, especially at higher temperatures, which reduces the solubility of hydrogen sulphide so that the foul-smelling gas is released.

$$HS^-(aq) + H_2O(l) \rightleftharpoons H_2S(aq) + OH^-(aq)$$

$$H_2S(aq) \rightleftharpoons H_2S(g) + aq$$

Exercise 58

(a) Acid strength increases as the group is descended.

(b) The Group VI hydrides act as acids by ionizing in the following manner:

$$H_2X(aq) + H_2O(l) \rightleftharpoons H_3O^+(aq) + HX^-(aq)$$

Since the size of the Group VI atom, X, increases as the group is descended we expect the length of the H—X bond to increase and its strength to decrease. It is reasonable to suppose, therefore, that protons might be more readily removed as the group is descended, i.e. H_2X becomes more acidic.

(Note that bond polarity decreases, and this might seem to reduce the chance of proton removal but, as you have seen elsewhere, bond strength is usually more important than polarity.)

Exercise 59

(a) The H_2O_2 molecule has the structure shown on the right.

This is commonly called an 'open book' or 'skew-chain' structure.

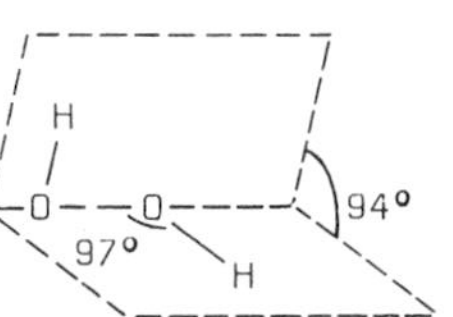

(b) Hydrogen peroxide is stable with respect to decomposition to the elements, as indicated by high negative values of $\Delta H_f^{\ominus}$ and $\Delta G_f^{\ominus}$. However, it is unstable with respect to decomposition to water and oxygen and this reaction can occur explosively.

$$2H_2O_2(l) \rightleftharpoons 2H_2O(l) + O_2(g)$$

(c) In the liquid state, hydrogen peroxide is even more highly associated via hydrogen bonding than is water. These strong intermolecular forces give pure hydrogen peroxide its high viscosity and boiling-point.

(d) Hydrogen peroxide might be expected to be weakly acidic. Since each oxygen atom shares electrons with only one hydrogen atom, the O—H bond polarity might be expected to be a little greater than it is in water, allowing proton donation to occur more readily.

Exercise 60

(a) (i) Reversing equation (1) and adding equation (5) gives:

$$H_2S(aq) + H_2O_2(aq) \rightarrow 2H_2O(l) + S(s)$$

(ii) Reversing equation (2) and adding equation (5) gives:

$$2I^-(aq) + H_2O_2(aq) + 2H^+(aq) \rightarrow I_2(aq) + 2H_2O(l)$$

(iii) Reversing equation (3), multiplying by 5, and adding twice equation (4) gives:

$$5H_2O_2(aq) + 2MnO_4^-(aq) + 6H^+(aq) \rightarrow 5O_2(g) + 2Mn^{2+}(aq) + 8H_2O(l)$$

(b) Reversing equation (3) and adding equation (5) gives:-

$$2H_2\overset{-1}{O_2}(aq) \rightarrow 2H_2\overset{-2}{O}(l) + \overset{0}{O_2}(g)$$

(c) Equations (4) and (5) suggest that hydrogen peroxide would oxidize $Mn^{2+}(aq)$ to $MnO_4^-(aq)$. But equations (3) and (4) suggest that the $MnO_4^-(aq)$ produced would be reduced again to $Mn^{2+}(aq)$ by more hydrogen peroxide. The net result could be the disproportionation of hydrogen peroxide as shown in (b) above.

Exercise 61

(a) Sulphur dioxide

Sulphur trioxide

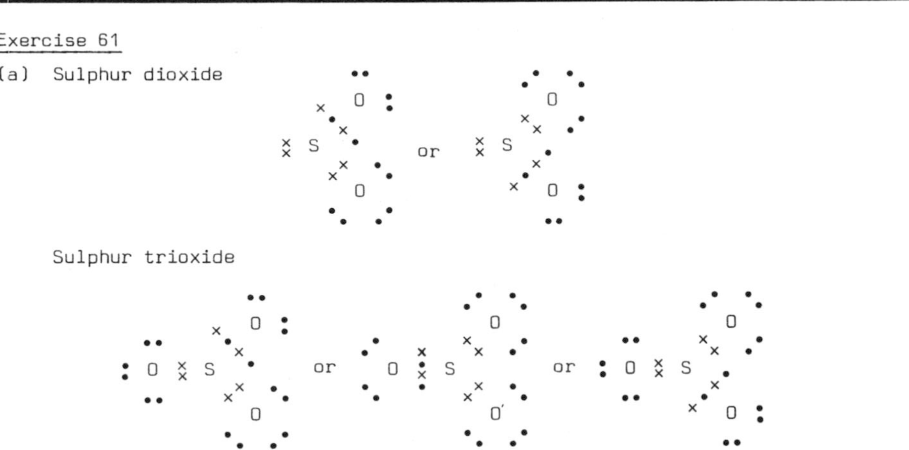

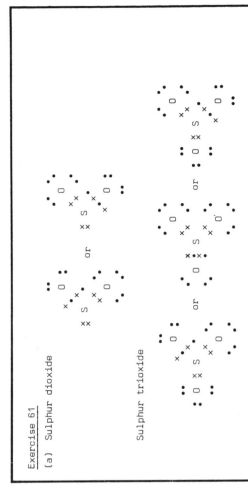

(b) The electrons in the double bonds shown in (a) are delocalized over the whole molecule. This gives two identical S—O bonds in sulphur dioxide and three identical S—O bonds in sulphur trioxide.

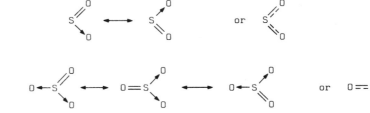

(c) SO_2 has an angular ('dog-leg') shape; SO_3 is trigonal planar (triangular). In each case, the O—S—O bond angles are close to 120°.

Exercise 62

(a) (i)

	$E^\ominus/V$
$SO_4^{2-}(aq) + 4H^+(aq) + 2e^- \rightleftharpoons SO_2(aq) + 2H_2O(l)$	+0.17
$MnO_4^-(aq) + 8H^+(aq) + 5e^- \rightleftharpoons Mn^{2+}(aq) + 4H_2O(l)$	+1.51

$\therefore$ $SO_2(aq)$ could reduce acidified $MnO_4^-(aq)$

(ii)

	$E^\ominus/V$
$SO_4^{2-}(aq) + 4H^+(aq) + 2e^- \rightleftharpoons SO_2(aq) + 2H_2O(l)$	+0.17
$Fe^{3+}(aq) + e^- \rightleftharpoons Fe^{2+}(aq)$	+0.77

$\therefore$ $SO_2(aq)$ could reduce $Fe^{3+}(aq)$

(iii)

	$E^\ominus/V$
$SO_4^{2-}(aq) + 4H^+(aq) + 2e^- \rightleftharpoons SO_2(aq) + 2H_2O(l)$	+0.17
$Cl_2(aq) + 2e^- \rightleftharpoons 2Cl^-(aq)$	+1.36

$\therefore$ $SO_2(aq)$ could reduce $Cl_2(aq)$

(iv)

	$E^\ominus/V$
$SO_4^{2-}(aq) + 4H^+(aq) + 2e^- \rightleftharpoons SO_2(aq) + 2H_2O(l)$	+0.17
$Cr_2O_7^{2-}(aq) + 14H^+(aq) + 6e^- \rightleftharpoons 2Cr^{3+}(aq) + 7H_2O(l)$	+1.33

$\therefore$ $SO_2(aq)$ could reduce $Cr_2O_7^{2-}(aq)$

(b) (i) Reversing the first equation, multiplying by five and adding twice the second equation gives:

$$5SO_2(aq) + 2H_2O(l) + 2MnO_4^-(aq) \rightarrow 5SO_4^{2-}(aq) + 4H^+(aq) + 2Mn^{2+}(aq)$$

(ii) Reversing the first equation and adding twice the second gives:

$$SO_2(aq) + 2H_2O(l) + 2Fe^{3+}(aq) \rightarrow SO_4^{2-}(aq) + 4H^+(aq) + 2Fe^{2+}(aq)$$

(iii) Reversing the first equation and adding the second gives:

$$SO_2(aq) + 2H_2O(l) + Cl_2(aq) \rightarrow SO_4^{2-}(aq) + 4H^+(aq) + 2Cl^-(aq)$$

(iv) Reversing the first equation, multiplying by three, and adding the second equation gives:

$$3SO_2(aq) + Cr_2O_7^{2-}(aq) + 2H^+(aq) \rightarrow 3SO_4^{2-}(aq) + 2Cr^{3+}(aq) + H_2O(l)$$

(c) Reaction (iv) forms a useful test for gaseous sulphur dioxide. A strip of filter paper moistened with acidified potassium dichromate(VI) solution turns green in contact with the gas.

Exercise 63

(a) $K_1 = 1.6 \times 10^{-2}$ mol dm^{-3} $\quad$ $pK_1 = 1.8$
$K_2 = 6.2 \times 10^{-8}$ mol dm^{-3} $\quad$ $pK_2 = 7.2$

(b) HSO_3^-, hydrogensulphite ion; SO_3^{2-}, sulphite ion

(Strictly, sulphite is tetraoxosulphate(IV), but this is not recommended at this level.)

(c) $H_2SO_4(aq) \rightleftharpoons H^+(aq) + HSO_4^-(aq)$

$HSO_4^-(aq) \rightleftharpoons H^+(aq) + SO_4^{2-}(aq)$

(d) K_1 = 'very large' $\quad$ pK_1 = 'minus infinity'
$K_2 = 1.0 \times 10^{-2}$ mol dm^{-3} $\quad$ $pK_2 = 2.0$

(e) Sulphuric acid is a stronger acid than sulphurous. However, sulphurous acid is regarded as fairly strong in respect of its first ionization.

(It is interesting to note that it is only the first ionization of sulphuric acid which is virtually complete in aqueous solution.)

Exercise 64

(a)

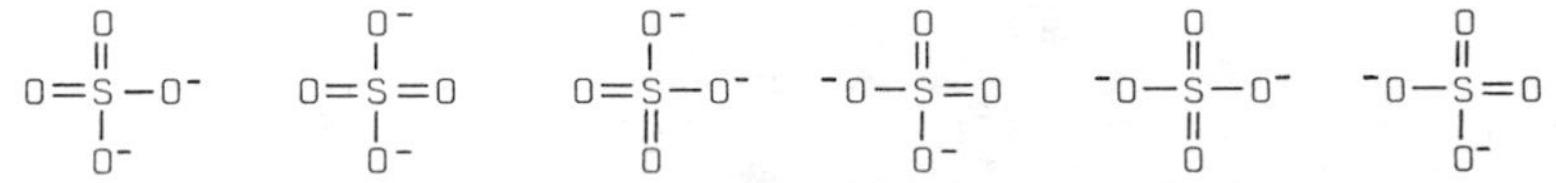

```
   O         O-        O-        O         O         O
   ||        |         |         ||        ||        ||
O=S-O-    O=S=O     O=S-O-   -O-S=O    -O-S-O-   -O-S=O
   |         |         ||        |         ||        |
   O-        O-        O         O-        O         O-
```

All the bonding electrons are delocalized so that all four bonds are identical. Repulsion between the bonding electrons gives a symmetrical tetrahedral molecule.

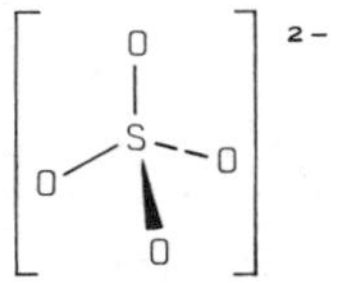

$[SO_4]^{2-}$ (tetrahedral)

(b) The SO_3^{2-} might be expected to be trigonal pyramidal, based on the tetrahedral shape of SO_4^{2-} but with one oxygen atom replaced by a lone pair of electrons.

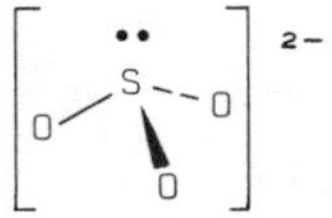

$[SO_3]^{2-}$ (trigonal pyramidal, lone pair on S)

(c) The lone pair on the sulphur atom in SO_3^{2-} is used to make an S—S bond with a sulphur atom.

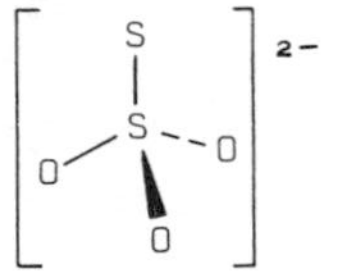

$[S{-}SO_3]^{2-}$

Experiment 3. Questions

1. (a) Sulphur dioxide is released from 'sulphurous acid' on heating.

$$\overset{+4}{S}O_3^{2-}(aq) + 2H^+(aq) \rightarrow \overset{+4}{S}O_2(g) + H_2O(l)$$

(b) No reaction.

(c) Sulphur is slowly precipitated and sulphur dioxide released.

$$\overset{+2}{S_2}O_3^{2-}(aq) + 2H^+(aq) \rightarrow \overset{+4}{S}O_2(g) + \overset{0}{S}(s) + H_2O(l)$$

(d) No reaction.

(e) Silver sulphite is precipitated, but this dissolves initially in excess sulphite to form a complex ion.

(i) $\overset{+4}{S}O_3^{2-}(aq) + 2Ag^+(aq) \rightarrow Ag_2\overset{+4}{S}O_3(s)$

(ii) $Ag_2\overset{+4}{S}O_3(s) + \overset{+4}{S}O_3^{2-}(aq) \rightarrow 2[Ag\overset{+4}{S}O_3]^-$

(f) Silver sulphate is precipitated, but this is moderately soluble and so the precipitate is not heavy.

$$Ag^+(aq) + SO_4^{2-}(aq) \rightarrow Ag_2SO_4(s)$$

(g) Silver thiosulphate is precipitated but this dissolves initially in excess thiosulphate to form a complex ion. The precipitate decomposes to black silver sulphide.

(i) $\overset{+2}{S_2}O_3^{2-}(aq) + 2Ag^+(aq) \rightarrow Ag_2\overset{+2}{S_2}O_3(s)$

(ii) $Ag_2\overset{+2}{S_2}O_3(s) + 3\overset{+2}{S_2}O_3^{2-}(aq) \rightarrow 2[Ag(\overset{+2}{S_2}O_3)_2]^{3-}$

(iii) $Ag_2\overset{+2}{S_2}O_3(s) + H_2O(l) \rightarrow Ag_2\overset{-2}{S}(s) + 2H^+(aq) + \overset{+6}{S}O_4^{2-}(aq)$

(h) It is not clear what happens in this reaction. It is probably similar to (g) with an unstable complex ion producing silver sulphide.

(i) Iodine is reduced to iodide ions and sulphite ions are oxidized to sulphate ions

$$I_2(aq) + \overset{+4}{S}O_3^{2-} + H_2O(l) \rightarrow 2I^-(aq) + \overset{+6}{S}O_4^{2-}(aq) + 2H^+(aq)$$

(j) No reaction.

(k) Iodine is reduced to iodide ions and sulphite ions are oxidized to tetrathionate ions. (You should recall this reaction from Unit I2 - it is used in titrations.)

$$I_2(aq) + 2\overset{+2}{S_2}O_3^{2-}(aq) \rightarrow 2I^-(aq) + \overset{+2.5}{S_4}O_6^{2-}(aq)$$

(As you should recall, the overall oxidation number of 2.5 for S in $S_4O_6^{2-}$ arises because two sulphur atoms have oxidation number -1 and two have +6.)

(l) Iodide ions (from the potassium iodide) are oxidized to iodine and peroxodisulphate ions are reduced to sulphate ions.

$$2I^-(aq) + \overset{+6}{S_2}O_8^{2-}(aq) \rightarrow I_2(aq) + 2\overset{+6}{S}O_4^{2-}(aq)$$

[Sulphur in $S_2O_8^{2-}$ appears to have an oxidation number of +7, given by $\frac{1}{2}(-2 + 16) = 7$. However, as the name suggests, the ion contains an O—O link, which means that two of the oxygen atoms have an oxidation number of -1 and it is these atoms which are reduced.]

(m), (n) and (o) No reaction.

Experiment 3. Specimen results

Results Table 5

Test	Na_2SO_3	Na_2SO_4	$Na_2S_2O_3$	$Na_2S_2O_8$	'X'
1. Warm with dilute hydrochloric acid.	No reaction in cold. Bubbles of gas on warming. Choking smell. $K_2Cr_2O_7$ paper turned green. (SO_2 produced.)	No visible reaction.	Solution turned slightly cloudy, denser when warm. Choking smell. $K_2Cr_2O_7$ paper turned green. (SO_2 produced.)	No visible reaction.	Solution turned slightly cloudy, denser when warm. Choking smell. $K_2Cr_2O_7$ paper turned green. (SO_2 produced.)
2. Add silver nitrate solution.	Initial white ppt. dissolved on shaking. With more $AgNO_3$ a dense white ppt. remained.	No reaction at first, then a faint white ppt. appeared.	Initial white ppt. dissolved on shaking. With more $AgNO_3$ the ppt. remained and turned yellow, brown and black.	Blackish ppt. formed slowly.	Initial white ppt. dissolved on shaking. With more $AgNO_3$ the ppt. remained and turned yellow, brown and black.
3. Add iodine solution (in aqueous potassium iodide).	The brown colour was immediately discharged. (Iodine reduced.)	No visible reaction.	The brown colour was immediately discharged. (Iodine reduced.)	The brown colour became darker. (Iodide oxidized.)	The brown colour was immediately discharged. (Iodine reduced.)
4. Add potassium iodide solution.	No visible reaction.	No visible reaction.	No visible reaction.	A dark brown solution was formed. (Iodide oxidized.)	No visible reaction.
5. Add iron(III) chloride solution and dilute acid. Warm and add sodium hydroxide solution.	A dark red-brown solution was formed which became almost colourless when hot. Addition of alkali gave a green ppt. (Fe^{3+} reduced.)	A yellow solution was formed which darkened a little on warming. Addition of alkali gave a red-brown ppt. (Fe^{3+} not reduced.)	A dark purple solution was formed which cleared when hot and then became cloudy. Addition of alkali gave a green ppt. (Fe^{3+} reduced.)	A yellow solution was formed which darkened a little on warming. Addition of alkali gave a red-brown ppt. (Fe^{3+} not reduced.)	A dark red-brown solution was formed which became almost colourless when hot. Addition of alkali gave a green ppt. (Fe^{3+} reduced.)
6. Heat a small portion of the solid salt.	Crystals turned white & gave off a steamy vapour which condensed on the upper tube (H_2O). White residue turned yellow on strong heating.	A colourless liquid was rapidly formed, which boiled to give a steamy vapour (H_2O) and a white residue. No further reaction.	A colourless liquid was rapidly formed which boiled to give a steamy vapour (H_2O). The yellowish residue turned brown & gave a black viscous liquid.	The solid melted to a colourless liquid. Bubbles of gas relit a glowing splint. (O_2.)	

(p) The same reaction as in (l).

(q) An unstable complex ion of uncertain composition is formed initially but this decomposes. Iron(III) ions are reduced to iron(II) ions and sulphite ions are oxidized to sulphate ions. The green precipitate is iron(II) hydroxide.

$$2Fe^{3+}(aq) + \overset{+4}{S}O_3^{2-}(aq) + H_2O(l) \rightarrow 2Fe^{2+}(aq) + \overset{+6}{S}O_4^{2-}(aq) + 2H^+(aq)$$

$$Fe^{2+}(aq) + 2OH^-(aq) \rightarrow Fe(OH)_2(s)$$

(r) and (t) No reaction initially. The red-brown precipitate is iron(III) hydroxide.

$$Fe^{3+}(aq) + 3OH^-(aq) \rightarrow Fe(OH)_3(s)$$

(s) An unstable complex ion of uncertain composition is formed initially. Iron(III) ions are reduced to iron(II) ions and thiosulphate ions are oxidized to tetrathionate ions. The green precipitate is iron(II) hydroxide.

$$2Fe^{3+}(aq) + 2\overset{+2}{S_2}O_3^{2-}(aq) \rightarrow 2Fe^{2+}(aq) + \overset{+2.5}{S_4}O_6^{2-}(aq)$$

$$Fe^{2+}(aq) + 2OH^-(aq) \rightarrow Fe(OH)_2(s)$$

(u) Water of crystallization is released. There is possibly some slight decomposition to sulphur (and sulphur dioxide?).

(v) Water of crystallization is released rapidly, in sufficient quantity to dissolve the salt. The anhydrous sulphate does not decompose at the temperature of a Bunsen burner.

(w) Water of crystallization is released rapidly, sufficient to dissolve the salt. The anhydrous thiosulphate decomposes, releasing sulphur, which melts to a thick black liquid.

(x) The peroxodisulphate releases oxygen on heating and forms the sulphate and sulphur dioxide.

$$\overset{+6}{S_2}O_8^{2-}(aq) \rightarrow \overset{+6}{S}O_4^{2-}(aq) + O_2(g) + \overset{+4}{S}O_2(g)$$

2. Reaction (c), between thiosulphate and hydrogen ions, is disproportionation. [Also (g) (iii) and (w).]

3. (i) The peroxodisulphate ion is the strongest oxidizing agent.

   (ii) The sulphite ion and the thiosulphate ion are strong reducing agents. [Thiosulphate is stronger, under standard conditions, but this is not evident in these reactions.]

   (iii) The sulphate ion is the most stable - it remains intact throughout these tests.

4. Dissolve the two salts in water. Add dilute hydrochloric acid and barium chloride solution to each. The sulphate gives a dense white precipitate of barium sulphate.

$$Ba^{2+}(aq) + SO_4^{2-}(aq) \rightarrow BaSO_4(s)$$

Barium sulphite is soluble in dilute acids but there may be a faint precipitate due to sulphate impurities formed by oxidation.

5. The reactions of X suggest that thiosulphate ions are formed by heating sulphur and sulphite ions.

$$S(s) + SO_3^{2-}(aq) \rightarrow S_2O_3^{2-}(aq)$$

The reaction takes some time to complete, so the prepared solution still contained some sulphite.

Exercise 65

(a) There is a gradual increase in the first four ionization energies in line with the increasing effective nuclear pull due to the removal of the outer 4*p* electrons. A significant jump occurs between the 4th and 5th ionization energies coinciding with the removal of a 4*s* electron which is more firmly held to the nucleus than are the *p* electrons. The jump between the 6th and 7th ionization energy results from the removal of an electron from an inner quantum shell.

(b) (i)

```
  ••          ••
 ×O  ×Se ×  O×
  ••   ×•×•   ••
       •O•
```

(ii) Bond *b* has more double-bond character (greater electron density) than bond *a*.

(c)

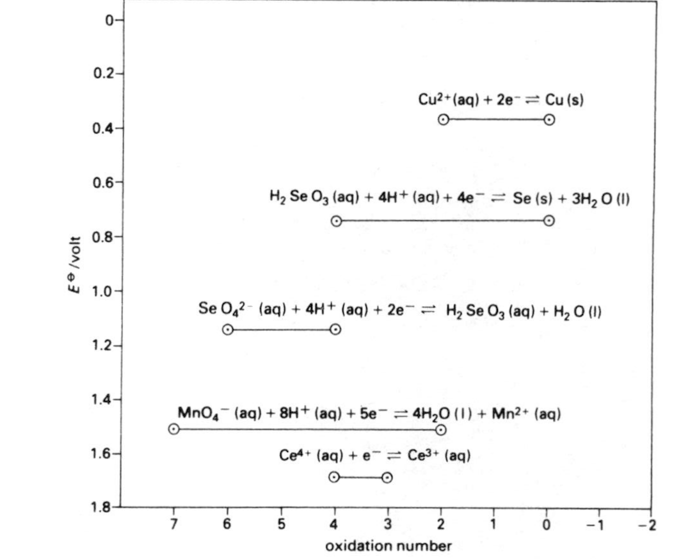

(d) (i) The purple MnO_4^- solution would be decolorized.

(ii) $2Ce^{4+}(aq) + H_2SeO_3(aq) + H_2O(l) \rightarrow 2Ce^{3+}(aq) + SeO_4^{2-}(aq) + 4H^+(aq)$

(e) (i) $Cu(s)|Cu^{2+}(aq)¦[SeO_4^{2-}(aq) + 4H^+(aq)], [H_2SeO_3(aq) + H_2O(l)]|Pt(s)$

(ii) $\Delta E^\ominus = +1.15\ V - (+0.36\ V) = +0.79\ V$

Exercise 66

(a) (i) Dissolution in this context means dissolving.

(ii) Flocculants are substances which encourage small solid particles in suspension to aggregate into larger particles as tufts, flakes or cloudy masses.

(iii) Calcination is prolonged heating of a solid to change its chemical composition. In this case, aluminium hydroxide (Gibbsite) is converted to the oxide with release of water vapour.

(b) (i) The main ingredients of red mud are iron oxides, sodium aluminium silicate, titanium oxide and various other metal oxides.

(ii) Iron(III) oxide gives red mud its colour.

(iii) Al_2O_3 is an amphoteric oxide and dissolves in sodium hydroxide solution to form aluminates. The other impurities tend to be insoluble, thus filtration separates the aluminate solution from the residue.

(iv) The silica (SiO_2) component of bauxite dissolves in the alkali to form silicates, e.g. Na_2SiO_3, but this is precipitated out as sodalite ($Na_2O{\cdot}Al_2O_3{\cdot}2SiO_2$) by reaction with sodium aluminate $NaAlO_2$.

$$Na_2SiO_3 + NaAlO_2 \rightarrow Na_2O{\cdot}Al_2O_3{\cdot}2SiO_2$$

(c) (i) Alumina is dissolved in molten cryolite, Na_3AlF_6, before electrolysis.

(ii) Fluorides of lithium, calcium and aluminium, LiF, CaF_2 and AlF_3, are added in order to reduce the melting-point of the cryolite and improve the efficiency of the electrolysis process.

(iii) Cathode reaction: $4AlF_6^{3-} + 12e^- + 4Al + 24F^-$

Anode reaction: $6AlOF_2^- + 3C + 24F^- \rightarrow 3CO_2 + 6AlF_6^{3-} + 12e^-$

Overall cell reaction: $2Al_2O_3 + 3C \rightarrow 4Al + 3CO_2$

(iv) Very little cryolite is used up because the AlF_6^{3-} ions produced from the cryolite are regenerated at the anode.

(d) (i) The anode is made of carbon because, by making its combustion part of the overall cell reaction, the total energy input is reduced by a half.

(ii) The anodes are renewed because during the process they are converted to carbon dioxide.

(iii) Continuous renewal is preferred because this saves both time and energy. Simple replacement of the anodes would require the current to be switched off and would allow a lot of heat to escape from the cell.

(e) See above right.

Exercise 66 (continued)

(e)

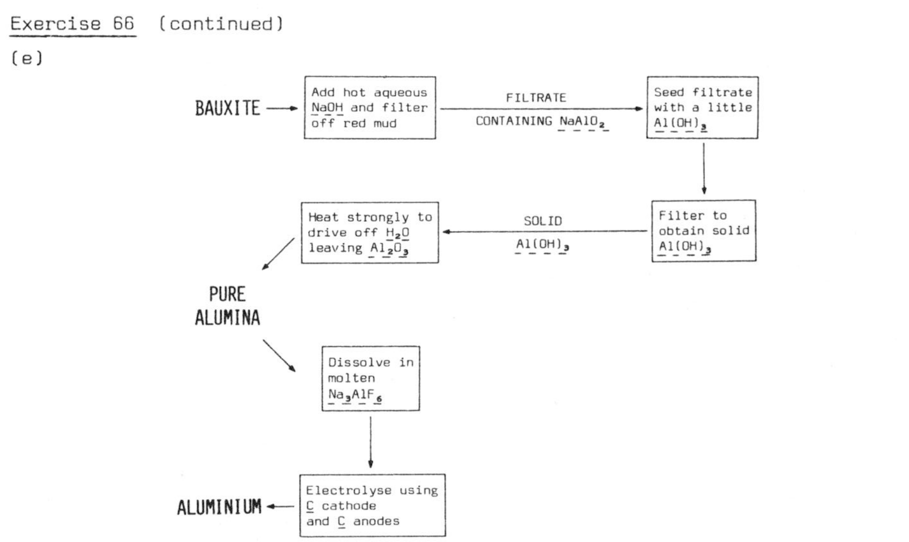

BAUXITE
Add hot aqueous NaOH and filter off red mud
FILTRATE CONTAINING NaAlO2
Seed filtrate with a little Al(OH)3
Filter to obtain solid Al(OH)3
SOLID Al(OH)3
Heat strongly to drive off H2O leaving Al2O3
PURE ALUMINA
Dissolve in molten Na3AlF6
Electrolyse using C cathode and C anodes
ALUMINIUM

Exercise 67

(a) Disposal of red mud is a major problem because the vast amounts produced create environmental and economic problems. It is estimated that a lagoon of approximately 1 km^2 in area is required for a plant processing 3.3 m tons of bauxite per year.

(b) Attempts have been made to convert red mud into building materials and cement and to extract titanium from it but this has not yet significantly reduced the amount of mud.

(c) Aluminium is a very important modern-day metal and the increase in its production is in line with the extra demand created by an increasing world population and higher living standards.

(d) Aluminium is used to make military machines and weapons as well as important industrial and everyday goods. For these reasons, the U.S.A. and the U.S.S.R. have stockpiled bauxite to avoid medium-term shortages.

(e) Alunite, $KAl_3(SO_4)_2(OH)_6$ and nepheline, $KNaAlSiO_4$ have been used as non-bauxite materials in the U.S.S.R.

(f) The factors which have led to a renewed interest in non-bauxite sources of aluminium include:

(i) reserves and resources of bauxite which are less secure;

(ii) increased costs and other drawbacks in the use of the Bayer Process for processing lower quality ores (Al < 40%, Si > 7%), and disposal of red mud.

(g) Reserves of bauxite are quite high; the cost of changing the technology would be great; investment in existing plant is high; long-term agreements between supplying and using countries should be honoured.

Experiment 4. Questions

1. Anodized aluminium is (a) less shiny than non-anodized aluminium, (b) a poor conductor on the surface, and (c) easily dyed.

2. The anodized layer adds some resistance to the circuit. The resistance of the solution increases as the temperature falls because the ions move less readily.

3. (a) Anodized aluminium is used to increase resistance to corrosion, e.g. in window frames, and for articles made more attractive to the consumer by dyeing, e.g. saucepan lids.

   (b) Anodized aluminium is not used for articles where electrical contacts need to be made.

Exercise 68

(a) (i) At approximately 1200 K the lines cross for the reactions:

$$2Zn(s) + O_2(g) \rightleftharpoons 2ZnO(s)$$

$$2C(s) + O_2(g) \rightleftharpoons 2CO(g)$$

This means that at 1200 K, $\Delta G^{\ominus}$ is zero for the reaction:

$$ZnO(s) + C(s) \rightleftharpoons Zn(s) + CO(g)$$

At lower temperatures, $\Delta G^{\ominus}$ is positive and the reaction is not feasible. At temperatures greater than 1200 K, $\Delta G^{\ominus}$ is negative and the reaction is feasible.

(ii) C could reduce FeO at temperatures above 1050 K approximately. Reasoning as in (i).

(iii) C could reduce Al_2O_3 at temperatures above 2400 K approximately. Reasoning as in (i).

(b) The minimum temperature required for the reduction of aluminium oxide by carbon is too high for economic production. (Even if no alternative were available, this method would not be suitable because aluminium combines with carbon at high temperatures to form the carbide, Al_4C_3.)

Exercise 69

(a) (i) Two of the following: ammonium nitrate, NH_4NO_3, sodium nitrate, $NaNO_3$, ammonium sulphate $(NH_4)_2SO_4$, urea, $(NH_2)_2CO$, ammonium phosphate, $(NH_4)_3PO_4$.

(ii) Nylon, or Acrilan, or Melamine.

(b) (i) In the methane-steam reforming process, methane and steam react together over a nickel-on-refractory catalyst.

$$CH_4(g) + H_2O(g) \rightleftharpoons CO(g) + 3H_2(g)$$

The gases in the equilibrium shown above are heated to a temperature of 1100 °C as they leave the steam reformer. This is done by burning methane in the steam reformer. This raised temperature displaces the equilibrium well over to the right and thus increases the yield of hydrogen.

(ii) The word 'refractory' is usually used to describe a compound such as an inorganic oxide which has a high melting-point.

(Continued above right.)

Exercise 69 (continued)

(b) (iii) The reaction must be endothermic since an increase in temperature favours the formation of hydrogen. Le Chatelier's principle tells us that equilibrium will shift in such a direction as to counteract the imposed change; in this case to reduce the temperature again.

$$CH_4(g) + H_2O(g) \rightarrow CO(g) + 3H_2(g); \quad \Delta H^{\ominus} \text{ is positive.}$$

(iv)

$$K_p = \frac{p_{CO} \times p^3_{H_2}}{p_{CH_4} \times p_{H_2O}}$$

When the total pressure of the steam is increased, the equilibrium is disturbed. A new equilibrium position is established by producing more CO and H_2, i.e. the partial pressure of hydrogen increases.

(c) (i) The two crucial factors in the synthesis of ammonia are:

(1) the position of equilibrium for the synthesis reaction and

(2) the rate at which equilibrium is attained.

(ii) The catalyst used consists of metallic iron with small amounts of various refractory oxides (i.e. alumina, silica and magnesium oxide) and promoted by potassium hydroxide.

The catalyst is made by melting together the above ingredients in their oxide form (i.e. using Fe_3O_4 instead of iron) and then casting the melt. The resulting sheet is broken up into 5-10 mm pieces and finally reduced. This produces small iron crystallites separated by amorphous refractory oxides, and partly covered with potassium hydroxide.

(iii) Water vapour tends to make the catalyst ineffective in two ways. Firstly, it chemisorbs on the surface of the catalyst, and secondly it alters the structure of the catalyst resulting in larger iron crystallites. Both these factors reduce the exposed iron surface area and thus reduce catalytic activity. Water vapour can enter the catalyst directly, or indirectly in the form of CO and CO_2. Both these gases will be hydrogenated to methane and water vapour over the catalyst.

(d) The economy of the ammonia synthesis is partly determined by the rate of attainment of equilibrium and partly by the position of equilibrium.

The rate of attainment of equilibrium is determined by the catalyst, which is most effective between 400 °C and 540 °C. Unfortunately, high temperatures tend to displace the equilibrium to the left thus reducing the yield of ammonia. To displace the equilibrium in the opposite direction in order to increase the yield of ammonia, two operations are carried out. Firstly, pressures in the range 8 080-35 350 kPa are used and secondly, the ammonia is liquefied and removed from the equilibrium.

The total power requirement is little affected by the choice of operating pressure within the range stated. More power is required to compress and re-circulate gases at higher pressures, but less is then required for the refrigeration plant.

However, lower operating pressures are increasingly favoured because they can be achieved by cheap steam-turbine compressors which use waste heat from elsewhere in the process. This gives a total energy efficiency of about 65% with most of the waste arising from the combustion of methane in the reformer.

Exercise 70

(a) (i) Higher temperatures give low yields of ammonia because the process is exothermic. (Also, the catalyst tends to sinter, which reduces its surface area.)

(ii) At lower temperatures, the rate of achieving equilibrium is too slow, even though the potential yield is greater.

(b) The cost of generating pressures in excess of 200 atmospheres is high, since such pressures are out of the range of cheap rotary gas compressors.

(c) Ammonia is separated by refrigerating to temperatures at which only ammonia liquefies.

(d) The heat exchanger cools the gas mixture after the exothermic reaction so that the operating temperature after recycling does not exceed 800 K.

(e) (i) $K_p = \dfrac{p^2_{NH_3}}{p_{N_2} \times p^3_{H_2}}$

(ii) The presence of argon reduces the partial pressure of ammonia and hence the yield. This is not due to a change in the equilibrium position but merely a 'dilution' effect.

(iii) Argon constitutes about 1% of the air intake but it is unaffected by any part of the process. Consequently, the amount of argon present increases as the gases are recycled.

(f) (i) The amount ratio of N_2 to H_2 is 1:3 in the feedstock and in the reactions; consequently, it is also 1:3 in the equilibrium mixture. Since partial pressure is proportional to amount,

$$p_{H_2} = 3p_{N_2} = \boxed{126\ \text{atm}}$$

(ii) Partial pressure of ammonia, $p_{NH_3} = p_T - p_{H_2} - p_{N_2}$

$$= (200 - 126 - 42)\text{atm} = \boxed{32\ \text{atm}}$$

$$\therefore\ \%\ \text{of}\ NH_3 = \frac{p_{NH_3}}{p_T} \times 100 = \frac{32\ \text{atm}}{200\ \text{atm}} \times 100 = \boxed{16\%}$$

(iii) The rate of reaction decreases as equilibrium is approached. This makes it uneconomic to leave the gas mixture in contact with the catalyst for equilibrium to be fully attained. A greater total production is achieved by continuous replacement of slowly-reacting mixture with faster-reacting feedstock.

Exercise 71

(a) $K_p = \dfrac{p^4_{NO} \times p^6_{H_2O}}{p^4_{NH_3} \times p^5_{O_2}}$

(b) Excess air is used for two reasons.

(i) It forces the equilibrium

$$4NH_3(g) + 5O_2(g) \rightleftharpoons 4NO(g) + 6H_2O(g)$$

over to the right giving an efficient conversion of ammonia.

(ii) Continued above right.

Exercise 71 (continued)

(b) (ii) It converts the NO produced to N_2O_4 and, in excess, shifts equilibrium to the right in the reaction:

$$2NO(g) + O_2(g) \rightleftharpoons N_2O_4(g)$$

(c) The first stage is operated at atmospheric pressure because high pressures would favour the back reaction.

(d) Despite the fact that the reaction is exothermic (better yield at low temperature), the relatively high temperature of 900 °C is necessary to initiate the reaction and to achieve a satisfactory rate of reaction.

(e) The gases are cooled in order to displace the equilibrium:

$$2NO(g) + O_2(g) \rightleftharpoons N_2O_4(g)$$

to the right thus allowing nitrogen monoxide to be more easily oxidized.

(f) An increase in temperature will shift the position of equilibrium to the right thus increasing the relative amount of NO_2. This can be deduced from the $\Delta G^{\ominus}$ values which become more negative with increasing temperature, thus making the forward reaction more favourable.

(g) Two significant factors that a manufacturer should have considered would be the cost of ammonia feedstock and the cost of power and equipment necessary to generate pressure. Eight atmospheres pressure throughout would increase the throughput of gases and improve the absorption of nitrogen dioxide. These benefits might be offset by a lower conversion efficiency of ammonia and the cost of installing and running compressors.

Exercise 72

(a) (i) $N_2(g) + 3H_2(g) \rightleftharpoons 2NH_3(g)$

The gas mixture, at 200 atm and 800 K, is passed over an iron catalyst promoted with potassium hydroxide and containing a small amount of mixed refractory oxides, e.g. Al_2O_3, SiO_2, MgO.

(ii) $4NH_3(g) + 5O_2(g) \rightleftharpoons 4NO(g) + 6H_2O(g)$

The ammonia is mixed with excess air and passed through a platinum/rhodium gauze (90% Pt) at 900 °C and atmospheric pressure (sometimes 8 atm).

(iii) $2NO(g) + O_2(g) \rightleftharpoons N_2O_4(g)$ [or $2NO_2(g)$]

The gases are cooled and mixed with more oxygen.

(iv) $3NO_2(g) + H_2O(l) \rightleftharpoons 2HNO_3(aq) + NO(aq)$

[Many texts give: $4NO_2(g) + 2H_2O(l) + O_2(g) \rightarrow 4HNO_3(aq)$]

The reaction mixture is compressed to eight atmospheres and passed up absorption towers down which water is flowing. The nitrogen monoxide is recycled.

(b) Hydrogen and nitrogen are in the correct ratio (3:1) for the reaction, which is not affected by the small amounts of methane and argon. The methane is a remnant from the methane steam-reforming process for making hydrogen and the argon is from the air.

The carbon monoxide is present in very small amounts, a necessary condition to prevent poisoning of the catalyst. Carbon monoxide reacts with hydrogen over the catalyst to form water which is adsorbed by the catalyst, making it ineffective.

Exercise 73

(a) (i) Sulphur dioxide is obtained by burning sulphur in air.

$S(s) + O_2(g) \rightarrow SO_2(g)$

Some sulphur trioxide is also produced but this does not matter if the SO_2 is being converted to sulphuric acid.

(ii) Sulphides are converted to sulphur dioxide by roasting in air. Iron pyrites, which behaves like a mixture of iron(II) sulphide and sulphur, is often used.

$4FeS_2(s) + 11O_2(g) \rightarrow 2Fe_2O_3(s) + 8SO_2(g)$

Other sulphides react in a similar way, e.g.

$2ZnS(s) + 3O_2(g) \rightarrow 2ZnO(s) + 2SO_2(g)$

(b) Home-produced anhydrite became a useful, or potentially useful, source of sulphur during war-time. Imports of elemental sulphur could be threatened by naval action, or the producer (U.S.A.) might restrict exports because of its own war-effort and concern about reserves. However, sulphur reserves are now known to be very large and the use of anhydrite is too expensive when elemental sulphur is readily available.

(c) The catalyst used in the contact process is vanadium(V) oxide (on silica gel).

(d) The impurities may 'poison' the catalyst, i.e. make it ineffective by preferential adsorption.

(e) Sulphur trioxide is not directly absorbed in water because it would start to combine with the water vapour over the surface, forming a mist of sulphuric acid droplets. This mist does not condense easily and it causes serious air pollution. Sulphur trioxide is therefore absorbed in 98% sulphuric acid so that the mist does not form.

$SO_3(g) + H_2SO_4(l) \rightarrow \underset{\text{oleum}}{H_2S_2O_7(l)}$

The oleum produced is then diluted with water:

$H_2S_2O_7(l) + H_2O(l) \rightarrow 2H_2SO_4(aq)$

(f) The sulphur trioxide is passed through a heat exchanger in order to cool it before it reacts with 98% sulphuric acid. The heat can be used to drive the plant equipment.

Exercise 74

(a) $K_p = \dfrac{p^2_{SO_3}}{p^2_{SO_2} \times p_{O_2}}$

(b) (i) If the pressure is increased at constant temperature the equilibrium shifts to the right in accordance with Le Chatelier's principle, i.e. the equilibrium shifts in such a way that the pressure decreases again towards the original pressure. Since 2 mol of SO_3 exerts less pressure than 2 mol of SO_2 and 1 mol of O_2, the equilibrium shifts to the right.

A better explanation is given by inspection of the equilibrium constant expressed in terms of mole fraction.

$$K_p = \frac{p^2_{SO_3}}{p^2_{SO_2} \times p_{O_2}} = \frac{X^2_{SO_3}/p^2}{X^2_{SO_2}/p^2 \times X_{O_2}/p} = \frac{1}{p} \times \frac{X^2_{SO_3}}{X^2_{SO_2} \times X^2_{O_2}}$$

It is clear from this expression that if the total pressure, p, is increased, the mole fraction of sulphur trioxide must also increase.

(ii) An increase in temperature at constant pressure shifts the equilibrium to the left since the back reaction is endothermic and the system absorbs the added energy in an endothermic reaction.

(c) The temperature used is approximately 450 °C. The pressure is atmospheric or slightly higher.

(d) Although the yield of sulphur trioxide is theoretically improved by the use of high pressure, satisfactory yields are obtained using atmospheric pressure. Compressors are expensive to install and run; they are used only if a significant improvement in yield can be made.

(e) The catalyst speeds up the rate of attainment of equilibrium (but does not alter the position of equilibrium).

Exercise 75

(a) (i) $S(s) + O_2(g) \rightarrow SO_2(g)$

Sulphur is burnt in air.

(ii) $2SO_2(g) + O_2(g) \rightleftharpoons 2SO_3(g)$

A dry mixture of pure sulphur dioxide and excess air at about atmospheric pressure is passed over a catalyst of vanadium(V) oxide at 450 °C.

(iii) $SO_3(g) + H_2SO_4(l) \rightarrow H_2S_2O_7(l)$

Sulphur trioxide is absorbed in 98% sulphuric acid.

(iv) $H_2S_2O_7(l) + H_2O(l) \rightarrow 2H_2SO_4(aq)$

The oleum is diluted with water.

(b) (i) The sample was taken after burning the sulphur but before the addition of more air for the conversion to sulphur trioxide.

(ii) The plant appears to be working well at this stage. About half the oxygen in the original air (20%) has been converted to sulphur dioxide and a trace of trioxide. Further conversion would be slow because the partial pressure of oxygen over the sulphur would be small.